SPOTLIGHT on LITERATURE

GRAMMAR MINILESSONS

INTEGRATED LANGUAGE ARTS
GRADES 6-8

Macmillan
McGraw-Hill

New York • Farmington

Macmillan/McGraw-Hill

A Division of The McGraw-Hill Companies

Macmillan/McGraw-Hill
1221 Avenue of the Americas
New York, New York 10020

Printed in the United States of America

ISBN: 0-02-181478-3 / 6-8

1 2 3 4 5 6 7 8 9   D B H   02 01 00 99 98 97 96

TABLE OF CONTENTS

GRAMMAR

Sentences

Nouns

Verbs

Pronouns

Adjectives and Adverbs

Prepositions, Conjunctions, and Interjections

Clauses and Verbals

Book of Minilessons, Grades 6–8

Macmillan/McGraw-Hill

MECHANICS

USAGE

Macmillan/McGraw-Hill

SENTENCES

> • A **sentence** is a group of words that expresses a complete thought.

When you use complete sentences, your writing will be clear to your reader. Be sure to use correct end punctuation.

Complete: *The Egyptians build pyramids.*

Not Complete: *Built huge pyramids.*

Try It!   Write *sentence* next to each group of words that is a sentence.

1. The early civilization of Egypt was noteworthy.   _____

2. The ancient Egyptians developed sophisticated irrigation systems. _____

3. Able to harness the Nile.   _____

4. Early rulers who were cruel.   _____

5. Slaves were used to build the pyramids.   _____

6. Rulers, along with their belongings, were buried in some pyramids. _____

7. Egyptians used several methods to preserve the bodies of the dead. _____

8. Mummies wrapped in cloth.   _____

9. Sealed in airtight containers.   _____

10. Egyptian religion believed in an afterlife.   _____

Write It!   Suppose you had to design a pyramid for an Egyptian ruler. Do some research on pyramids and write a short report about them. Be sure that each sentence expresses a complete thought and has the correct end punctuation.

TYPES OF SENTENCES

- A **declarative sentence** makes a statement. It ends with a period.
- An **interrogative sentence** asks a question. It ends with a question mark.
- An **imperative sentence** makes a command or request. It ends with a period.
- An **exclamatory sentence** expresses strong feeling. It ends with an exclamation mark.

When you write, vary the types of sentences you use. This will make your writing more interesting. Remember to punctuate sentences correctly.

Declarative Sentence:	*I like pasta very much.*
Interrogative Sentence:	*Have you ever had linguine?*
Imperative Sentence:	*Prepare the sauce right now.*
Exclamatory Sentence:	*Wow, this meal is beyond belief!*

Try It!   Add the correct end punctuation to each of the sentences.

1. Our school is having a pasta night to raise money   _____

2. Are you going to go to the pasta night   _____

3. There will be over twenty-five different kinds of pasta   _____

4. Wow, that's a lot of pasta   _____

5. Several of my friends are going to go   _____

6. Don't even think about missing this night   _____

7. Who is cooking all that pasta   _____

8. My favorite pasta is linguine with red clam sauce   _____

9. Good grief, I can't believe you would eat a clam   _____

10. Go out and buy a ticket right now   _____

Write It!   Write a description of a school event you attended. Be sure to use different types of sentences and punctuate them correctly.

Book of Minilessons, Grades 6–8
Skill

Macmillan/McGraw-Hill

SENTENCE FRAGMENTS

> • A **sentence fragment** does not express a complete thought. It lacks either a subject part or a predicate part.

When you write, be sure to use complete sentences. Sentence fragments will confuse your reader.

Fragment (lacks a predicate):   *Some friends of mine.*

Fragment (lacks a subject):   *Spent their vacation on a safari.*

Try It!   Add a subject or a predicate to each of the fragments to make the fragment a complete sentence.

1. Going on my first safari.   _____

2. Planned my safari for a long time.   _____

3. Were anxious to see the game preserves.   _____

4. The parents and their two teen-age children.   _____

5. The guide on the safari.   _____

6. Rode in jeeps and trucks.   _____

7. The herd of giraffes.   _____

8. Several elephants and their babies.   _____

9. A severe dust storm.   _____

10. Had to leave for the trip home.   _____

Write It!   Imagine that you could go on a trip of your choice. What would it be? Where would you go? Write a description of your ideal trip. Be sure to use complete sentences and to punctuate them correctly.

RUN-ON SENTENCES

> • A **run-on sentence** joins two or more sentences that should be written separately.

Be sure to avoid run-on sentences when you write. Rewrite each part of the run-on as a complete sentence so that your readers will not be confused.

Run-on: *Sojourner Truth was an enslaved woman she wrote about her experiences.*

Correct: *Sojourner Truth was an enslaved woman. She wrote about her experiences.*

Try It!   Write *run-on* next to each sentence that is a run-on sentence.

1. Sojourner Truth was born in New York in 1795.   _____

2. When she was born, her name was Isabella van Hardenbergh.   _____

3. She was named for her enslaver's family she objected to that.   _____

4. She changed her name when slavery was abolished in New York State because she wished to leave her past behind.   _____

5. Sojourner Truth believed in women's rights she opposed slavery.   _____

6. Women who were enslaved did hard work it was as hard as work that the men did.   _____

7. Sojourner Truth traveled throughout the North speaking for women's rights and equality.   _____

8. She chose the name Truth she thought her mission was to tell the truth about the hardships and evil of slavery.   _____

9. Sojourner Truth was a brave and honorable woman.   _____

10. She did much to expose the evils of slavery and to promote equality for women.   _____

Write It!   Find out more information about Sojourner Truth and write a short report about her. Be sure to check that your sentences are complete and that you have no run-on sentences in your report.

Macmillan/McGraw-Hill

COMPLETE SUBJECTS AND PREDICATES

> • The **complete subject** includes all the words that tell whom or what the sentence is about.
>
> • The **complete predicate** includes all the words that tell what the subject does or is.

When you write it is important that your sentences have both a complete subject and a complete predicate. Otherwise, you have written a sentence fragment, which may confuse your readers.

Complete Subject	Complete Predicate
The tiny spider	*was grey and delicate looking.*

Try It!   Draw one line under the complete subject and two lines under the complete predicate.

1. *Charlotte's Web* by E. B. White is a children's classic.

2. E. B. White was a published poet and essayist.

3. This noted writer wrote for the *New Yorker* magazine.

4. He entertained adult audiences for years.

5. White surprised everyone with his book about a pig named Wilbur.

6. Wilbur and Charlotte, the spider, become the best of friends.

7. The other characters in the barnyard were friends with them, too.

8. Fern is a spunky and loyal little girl in the story.

9. Fern takes care of Wilbur until he is a grown pig.

10. Charlotte saves Wilbur's life.

Write It!   What is your favorite book? Write a book report about it. Make sure that all of your sentences have both a complete subject and a complete predicate.

Macmillan/McGraw-Hill

SIMPLE SUBJECTS AND PREDICATES

> - The **simple subject** is the main word or words in the complete subject.
> - The **simple predicate** is the main word or words in the complete predicate.

When you write, be sure that your sentences are complete. If your sentences are not complete, your message will not be clear to your reader.

Simple Subject	Simple Predicate
Today's modern **elevator**	**was invented** *by Elisha Otis.*

Try It!   Draw one line under the simple subject. Draw two lines under the simple predicate.

1. Elisha Otis built a factory in New York.

2. The factory needed a lifting device for its employees.

3. This inventor drew a plan for such a device.

4. Otis named his first machine the "safety hoister."

5. The audience screamed in terror at the first demonstration of the elevator.

6. The first passenger elevator was built for a hotel.

7. Today elevators reach the topmost floors in buildings.

8. Some buildings have more than 100 floors.

9. Elevator inspectors inspect elevators every year.

10. Safety is a very important issue in elevators.

Write It!   Who is your favorite inventor? Write a short biographical sketch of the inventor. Make sure that your sentences are complete. You may want to have a friend check your work.

COMPOUND SUBJECTS AND PREDICATES

> • A **compound subject** is two or more simple subjects with the same predicate.
>
> • A **compound predicate** is two or more simple predicates with the same subject.
>
> • A **coordinating conjunction** such as *and, or,* or *but* connects the parts of a compound subject or predicate.

Using compound subjects and predicates can add variety to your writing.

Compound Subject: *Dorrie and Janet* went to the mall.

Compound Predicate: They *shopped and ate dinner at a nice restaurant.*

Try It!   Label each sentence with *CS* for compound subject or with *CP* for compound predicate. If the sentence does not have either, label it *N.*

1. The mall has many beautiful stores.   _____

2. The shoppers walk briskly and carry many packages.   _____

3. Parents and their children stroll along slowly.   _____

4. Did you see that huge bookstore?   _____

5. Janet will buy a gift and send it to her niece.   _____

6. Dorrie and her friend come to the mall at least once a month.   _____

7. They browse in the music store and buy several CDs.   _____

8. A huge tour bus has brought many customers to the mall.   _____

9. Janet, Dorrie, and the clerk are finding the right sizes.   _____

10. Customers and tourists talk to each other at the mall.   _____

Write It!   Have you ever been to a mall? What did you do there? Write a paragraph about a trip to the mall. Try to include sentences that have compound subjects and compound predicates in your paragraph.

Macmillan/McGraw-Hill

COMPOUND SENTENCES

- A **simple sentence** has one complete subject and one complete predicate.

- A **compound sentence** has two or more simple sentences joined by *and, but,* or *or,* preceded by a comma.

When you write, be sure that your sentences are complete and that you vary your sentences. Some sentences can be compound sentences.

Simple sentence: *The members of the school committee met today.*

Compound sentence: *The school committee met, and they voted quickly.*

Try It!   Label each sentence *simple* or *compound.*

1. The school committee was formed to deal with problems at Lake Middle School. _____

2. Sarah Hathaway is president, and she works hard at her job. _____

3. The committee has four representatives from our grade. _____

4. Don Hicks is the best representative, but he misses some meetings. _____

5. He takes very good notes, or he uses his tape recorder at meetings. _____

6. I ran for the committee, but I was defeated by Jane Harris. _____

7. Next year I will run again, and you can be my campaign manager. _____

8. The committee proposes many laws for us to consider. _____

9. It's just like government in action. _____

10. I will need a platform for next year, and I will start my campaign right now. _____

Write It!   Have you ever run for a school office or helped someone else? What would your platform be? Think of some issues and write a paragraph that persuades people to vote for you. Be sure to use some compound sentences in your paragraph.

COMPLEX SENTENCES

> • A **subordinate clause** is a group of words that has a subject and a predicate, but cannot stand alone as a complete sentence.
>
> • A **complex sentence** contains an independent clause, which is a group of words that can stand alone as a complete sentence, and one or more subordinate clauses.

When you write, remember to put a comma after the subordinate clause if it comes at the beginning of the sentence.

Before the colonists sailed, they made sure they had adequate supplies.

The colonists were fearful *because they did not know what to expect.*

Try It!   Draw one line under the subordinate clause.

1. Although they had good supplies, the colonists almost did not survive.

2. They faced many hardships because the voyage to America was long.

3. When they arrived at Jamestown, they found the winter harsh.

4. Native Americans helped them when they first arrived.

5. Though the Native Americans helped them, the colonists had to learn to survive on their own.

6. Though John Smith was a fine leader, he could not do it all.

7. The government of Jamestown had to be secure before other colonists would come from England.

8. If disease or sickness came to Jamestown, very few would be able to survive without doctors.

9. Professional people would not make the trip to America unless they could be sure of their safety.

10. When the colony survived its first year, everyone was ecstatic.

Write It!   Do some research about the Colonial period in American history. Write a short report about what you find. Share your report with a classmate. Can your classmate identify the complex sentences?

Macmillan/McGraw-Hill

ADJECTIVE AND ADVERB CLAUSES

> • An **adjective clause** is a subordinate clause that modifies, or describes, a noun or pronoun in the independent clause of a complex sentence.
>
> • An **adverb clause** modifies the verb in the independent clause of a complex sentence.

When you write, be sure to use a comma after an adverb clause that comes at the beginning of the sentence.

Adjective Clause: Sheri has a necklace *that is handmade.*

Adverb Clause: She has owned it *since she was very young.*

Try It!   Draw one line under the adjective or adverb clause. Draw two lines under the word it modifies.

1. Sheri loves her locket because her grandmother gave it to her.

2. When Sheri was a baby, her grandmother bought it for her.

3. It was her grandmother who found the locket in the antique store.

4. It had a small heart that reminded her of her new granddaughter.

5. Her grandmother bought it because Sheri had just been born.

6. She kept it until she was sure Sheri wouldn't swallow it!

7. Grandmother was a woman who was very concerned with safety.

8. Although Sheri wanted the locket now, her grandmother waited.

9. Sheri was nine years old before her grandmother gave her the locket.

10. Because she had to wait so long, Sheri treasured her locket more.

Write It!   Suppose you received a lovely gift from someone. Write a thank you letter for the gift. Then share your letter with a friend. Can your friend point out any adjective or adverb clauses?

Macmillan/McGraw-Hill

KINDS OF NOUNS

> • A **noun** is a word that names a person, place, thing, or idea.
>
> • A **common noun** names a nonspecific person, place, thing, or idea.
>
> • A **proper noun** names a specific person, place, thing, or idea. A proper noun begins with a capital letter.

When you write, be sure to capitalize proper nouns.

Common Noun	Proper Noun	Common Noun	Proper Noun
cousin	Linda	mountain	Mount Everest
month	July	city	Los Angeles
planet	Saturn	time	Ice Age

Try It!   Draw one line under each common noun and two lines under each proper noun.

1. Linda, my cousin, has visited almost every state.

2. Her favorite state is North Carolina.

3. It is one of the best places on Earth as far as she is concerned.

4. The Smoky Mountains are magnificent.

5. The trees, gently sloping foothills, and streams are beautiful.

6. A ranger took Linda and her friends on a tour of the hiking paths.

7. They found interesting samples of rocks while she walked the hills.

8. Many small towns in North Carolina have interesting crafts.

9. Beautiful carvings are made from wood by the people of Boone.

10. Asheville is the home of the Biltmore Mansion, a huge house built by the Vanderbilts.

Write It!   What is your favorite state in the United States? Is it the one in which you live? Write a description of your favorite state. Be sure to include some proper nouns.

SINGULAR AND PLURAL NOUNS

> - A **singular noun** is a noun that names one person, place, thing, or idea.
>
> - A **plural noun** is a noun that names more than one person, place, thing, or idea. Add *s* or *es* to most singular nouns to make them plural.

When you write make sure that you use plural nouns correctly.

Singular: girl   house   bush   civilization

Plural: girl*s*   house*s*   bush*es*   civilization*s*

Try It!   Draw one line under each singular noun. Draw two lines under each plural noun.

1. My favorite class in school is English.

2. Of all the classes I take, English is the most interesting.

3. We read a new book every week in my class.

4. Mysteries are my favorite books because I love to figure out who did it.

5. By the end of the semester, the class had read almost 50 books.

6. We have to report on the books we read each month.

7. One month, I read almost 800 pages.

8. In my report, I compared all the books I read.

9. My teacher thought my report was excellent.

10. The next month, my best friend and I wrote our reports together.

Write It!   Suppose that you and a friend are planning to do a school project together. Write a plan for your project. List the steps that you will follow. Then see if you can identify the singular and plural nouns in your plan.

Macmillan/McGraw-Hill

Name: _____   Date: _____

PROPER NOUNS—PEOPLE

> • A **proper noun** names a specific person, place, thing, or idea.
> • A proper noun begins with a capital letter.

When you write, be sure to begin each proper noun with a capital letter.

Senator Jill Evans   Cousin Marc   M. K. Jones   Liz Stone, M.S.

Try It!   Write each proper noun, using the correct capitalization.

1. mary kelly   _____

2. c. k. harrison   _____

3. general lawrence smith   _____

4. aunt sylvia   _____

5. leona pak, ph. d.   _____

6. riverhead fire department 6   _____

7. uncle milton   _____

8. george c. little   _____

9. chief joseph   _____

10. atlantic avenue   _____

Write It!   Think of a relative that you like very much. Write a paragraph about a time you spent together. Be sure to capitalize any proper nouns you use in your paragraph.

PROPER NOUNS—PLACES

> - A **proper noun** names a specific person, place, thing, or idea.
> - Capitalize all proper nouns.

When you write, you can use proper nouns when you wish to be more specific about places.

Australia   Sacramento   Pacific Ocean   Saturn

Try It!   Write each proper noun, using the correct capitalization. Then, on a separate sheet of paper, write a sentence using the proper noun.

1. phoenix, arizona   _____

2. france   _____

3. north america   _____

4. baltic sea   _____

5. empire state building   _____

6. bay bridge   _____

7. cascades national park   _____

8. washington monument   _____

9. milky way   _____

10. 1222 tulip lane   _____

Write It!   Have you ever visited a national park or a national monument? Write a travel brochure for a place you have visited or would like to visit. Be sure to capitalize all proper nouns.

POSSESSIVE NOUNS

- A **possessive noun** is a noun that names who or what has something.
- Use an **apostrophe** and *s* ('s) to form the possessive of most singular nouns and of plural nouns that do not end in *s*.
- Use only an **apostrophe** (') to form the possessive of plural nouns that end in *s*.

When you write, be sure to use apostrophes correctly with possessive nouns.

John's book   Marie's ball   the boys' toys   the children's hats

Try It!   Rewrite each phrase, using a possessive noun. Tell whether the possessive noun is singular or plural.

1. the collar of the dog _____

2. the votes of the judges _____

3. the poodle of the owner _____

4. the reactions of the audience _____

5. the barks of the contestants _____

6. the dog show of the state _____

7. the collie of Susan Kelly _____

8. the awards of the show _____

9. the ribbons of the winners _____

10. the first prize of the terrier _____

Write It!   Suppose you entered a favorite pet in a pet show. What would the experience be like? Write a paragraph that tells about this event. Be sure to punctuate correctly any possessive nouns that you use.

Macmillan/McGraw-Hill

COLLECTIVE NOUNS

- A **collective noun** names a group of people or things.
- When the collective noun refers to a group as a whole, use a singular verb.
- When the collective noun refers to the individual members of the group, use the plural form of the verb.

When you use collective nouns in your writing, be sure to use the correct form of the verb.

The *family talk* over their problems together. **plural**

The *family spends* a lot of time outdoors. **singular**

Try It! Draw one line under each collective noun. Tell whether it is singular or plural.

1. The staff believes in the new representative. _____

2. The team talk among themselves about the news. _____

3. The army marches at a steady pace. _____

4. The public is not in support of the invasion. _____

5. The group votes for the law in the next session. _____

6. The audience react in many different ways. _____

7. A committee sits quietly in the corner of the meeting room. _____

8. The jury is not in agreement about the verdict. _____

9. A crowd watches as the people file by. _____

10. The congress sits in session all next week. _____

Write It! Think of something that you like to do with a group. Write a paragraph about it. If you use any collective nouns in your paragraph, be sure that you use the correct form of the verb.

Macmillan/McGraw-Hill

APPOSITIVES

> - An **appositive** is a word or group of words that follows a noun and identifies or explains it.
> - Use commas to set off most appositives.

Be sure to set off most appositives that you use in your writing with commas.

Try-outs for *Alone in the City,* a delightful new comedy, will be held Tuesday.

Try It!   Underline the appositive in each sentence. Then add commas where they are needed.

1. Mr. Jones our drama teacher will hold try-outs tomorrow.

2. The role of Mona the biggest part in the play is the one I want.

3. Most of my friends wonderful actresses in every way are going to try out, too.

4. The play a comedy in three acts is just hysterical.

5. The playwright a new writer has written a great play.

6. Mona a girl alone in the city meets a strange old lady.

7. The strange old lady a real character won't leave Mona alone.

8. Mona a cautious girl doesn't know what to do.

9. She enlists the help of her friend a private detective.

10. The play a true theatrical treat will surprise and delight you.

Write It!   Have you seen a good movie or a great play lately or read a good book? Write a review of a movie, play, or book. If you use appositives, be sure to use the correct punctuation.

ACTION VERBS

> • An **action verb** is a word that expresses action.

In your writing, be sure to use vivid action verbs so that your reader will be interested in your writing. Remember that an action verb can express mental action as well as physical action.

Whales *swim* far out in the ocean.

They *leap* gracefully into the air despite their size.

The scientist *ponders* their great size.

Try It!   Underline the action verbs. Tell whether the action verb expresses mental or physical action.

1. The field and track events start at 9:00 A.M. on Tuesday.   _____

2. Everyone crowds onto the field.   _____

3. The sprinters crouch at the starting line.   _____

4. Coach Jenkins smiles at the crowds.   _____

5. Assistants place the hurdles on the track.   _____

6. The javelin throwers stand at attention.   _____

7. The temperature soars higher and higher.   _____

8. The relay racers speed around the track.   _____

9. Everyone enjoyed the day.   _____

10. I remembered the day for a long time.   _____

Write It!   Suppose you were participating in a track and field event. Which one would it be? Write a paragraph telling about the event you chose. Be sure to use vivid verbs in your paragraph.

LINKING VERBS

> - A **linking verb** connects the subject of a sentence with a predicate noun or a predicate adjective. A linking verb does not show action.
> - A **predicate noun** renames or identifies the subject.
> - A **predicate adjective** describes the subject.

In your writing, you can use various kinds of verbs, linking and action, to add variety to your written work.

The winner was *Teddy*.	**predicate noun**
The winner was *overjoyed*.	**predicate adjective**

Try It!   Draw one line under a linking verb. Draw two lines under an action verb.

1. The school essay contest began today.

2. Last year's winner was Leslie Cassidy.

3. She is an excellent writer and thinker.

4. Her essay was extremely well written.

5. Leslie helps others in her class.

6. The second-place winner was Jonathan Park.

7. I want the prize this year.

8. "Why Students Should Be Heard" is the title of my essay.

9. My essay is more humorous than others.

10. My brother laughed at some of the points in my essay.

Write It!   Is there an issue you feel strongly about? Write an essay that tries to convince your audience to feel as you do. Share your essay with a friend. Can your friend identify any linking verbs?

DIRECT OBJECTS, TRANSITIVE AND INTRANSITIVE VERBS

> - A **direct object** is a noun or pronoun in the predicate that receives the action of the verb.
> - A **transitive verb** has a direct object.
> - An **intransitive verb** does not have a direct object.

Keep in mind when you write that a direct object can be two or more nouns or pronouns.

The Spanish built *missions* in the United States.

They brought *religion* and *education* to the people of the area.

The teacher taught *him* and *me* about the missionaries.

Try It!   Draw one line under the verb. Draw two lines under any direct objects. Label the verbs *transitive* or *intransitive*.

1. Spanish missionaries taught their language to the Native Americans.   _____

2. They gave food and shelter to them as well.   _____

3. In return Native Americans received religious instruction.   _____

4. Mission life was very complex.   _____

5. Everyone said prayers in the morning and in the evening.   _____

6. Missionaries kept gardens inside the mission walls.   _____

7. Native Americans grew food for themselves and for the priests.   _____

8. Education was important to everyone.   _____

9. Many missions still stand today in California and Texas.   _____

10. The missions represent a part of our nation's history.   _____

Write It!   Conduct some research on Spanish missions of California and Texas. Write a short report about one mission. Make sure to use vivid and varied verbs in your report.

Macmillan/McGraw-Hill

INDIRECT OBJECTS

> • An **indirect object** is a noun or a pronoun in the predicate that answers the question *to whom? for whom? to what?* or *for what?* after an action verb.

When you write, remember that sentences with an indirect object must also have a direct object. Remember that both direct objects and indirect objects can be two or more words.

      indirect object   direct object

Sally gave *Jason* the history *book*.

    indirect direct   direct
    object   object   object

Jason showed *me* the *book* and the *report*.

Try It!   Draw one line under the indirect object. Draw two lines under the direct object.

1. Sally showed me a report on Greece.

2. She told the class some interesting facts about Greek warfare.

3. The Greek army offered its soldiers no choice.

4. The battles brought both sides much sorrow.

5. The wars caused Greece hardship and suffering.

6. Great heroes often gave each other grave wounds.

7. Achilles won his country freedom from oppression.

8. The Greek gods gave Achilles much good fortune.

9. Achilles brought his country fame and fortune.

10. Vulcan gave Achilles a magical set of armor.

Write It!   What is your favorite myth? Write a paragraph of explanation about your favorite myth. Then, share your paragraph with a classmate. Can your friend identify the direct and indirect objects in your writing?

ACTIVE AND PASSIVE VOICES

> - A verb is in the **active voice** when the subject of the sentence performs the action. Verbs in the active voice may or may not have a direct object.
>
> - A verb is in the **passive voice** when the subject of the sentence receives the action. Verbs in the passive voice do not have a direct object.

Using verbs in the active voice can make your writing stronger.

The hikers greeted the ranger.   **active voice**

The hikers were approached by the ranger.   **passive voice**

Try It!   Tell whether the verb in each sentence is in the active or passive voice.

1. The hikers were frightened by the rough trails.   _____

2. However, they struggled onward to the top of the foothill.   _____

3. At the top they were met by the other group of hikers.   _____

4. The hikers exchanged stories with each other.   _____

5. The hike had been planned by very experienced hikers.   _____

6. Great fun was had by all despite the difficulties.   _____

7. The campfire cast a rosy glow on the campers' faces.   _____

8. The stories were told in a very funny way.   _____

9. Bret was reduced to hysterical laughter at one point.   _____

10. The campers gave each other their addresses.   _____

Write It!   Describe the best camping, hiking, or field trip that you have had. When you have finished your description, look for any sentences in the passive voice. Change the verbs in those sentences to the active voice.

SUBJECT-VERB AGREEMENT

> - A verb must agree in number with its subject. Use a singular verb with a singular subject and a plural verb with a plural subject.
> - A verb must agree with its subject even if the verb comes before the subject or the verb is separated from the subject.

When you write, be sure that your subjects and verbs agree so that your reader will not be confused.

The **divers use** a great deal of equipment.

The team **leader uses** several pieces of heavy apparatus.

Did they use the aqualung?

Try It!   Underline the correct form of the verb in parentheses.

1. Jacques Cousteau (study, studies) life under the sea.

2. His assistants (help, helps) him on his voyages.

3. Divers (use, uses) aqualungs when they dive beneath the sea.

4. The experts (check, checks) the aqualungs very carefully.

5. Cousteau (give, gives) many lectures to students and to the public.

6. Members of the audience (ask, asks) him many questions.

7. (Is, Are) he happy to share his information?

8. The underwater explorers (find, finds) interesting facts about the sea.

9. They (spend, spends) hours under water.

10. Could you (live, lives) under water for a great length of time?

Write It!   Imagine that you were going to interview Jacques Cousteau. What questions would you ask him? Write five questions that you would like answered. Make sure that your subjects agree with your verbs.

PRESENT, PAST, AND FUTURE TENSES

> • The **present tense** of a verb tells that something is happening now or happens repeatedly.
>
> • The **past tense** of a verb shows an action that has already happened.
>
> • The **future tense** of a verb shows an action that will take place in the future.

When you write, be sure to use the correct verb tenses so that your reader will understand when the action is taking place.

I *see* the tall ships today.   **present tense**

I *saw* the tall ships yesterday.   **past tense**

I *will see* the tall ships again tomorrow.   **future tense**

Try It!   Draw one line under the verb. Tell the tense of the verb.

1. Sarah saw the ships in the harbor yesterday. _____

2. The ships had signal flags on them. _____

3. The flags will fly in the wind at sea. _____

4. The green and white flag flew above the mast. _____

5. The wind blows very hard in the North Atlantic. _____

6. Sarah draws her own flag designs. _____

7. Her brother gave her a book about flags when she was young. _____

8. Sarah will design a special flag for her dad's boat. _____

9. She also knows quite a bit about flag codes. _____

10. She explained flag codes to our class last year. _____

Write It!   Imagine that you had to design a secret code for some sailing ships. How would you go about it? Write an explanation. Make sure that you use correct verb tenses in your explanation.

Macmillan/McGraw-Hill

IRREGULAR VERBS

> • The past and past participle forms of **irregular verbs** do not end in *ed*.

Most past-tense verbs end in *ed,* but irregular verbs do not. When you write, make sure to use the correct form of an irregular verb. Refer to your textbook for charts that show irregular verb forms.

Present	Past	Past Participle
be (is, are)	was, were	(have, has, had) been
come	came	(have, has, had) come
bring	brought	(have, has, had) brought
sit	sat	(have, has, had) sat

Try It!   Underline the correct past or past participle form of the verb in parentheses.

1. The literary contest (was, has been) yesterday.

2. John (bring, brought) his poetry to the reading.

3. He (choose, chose) the environment as his subject.

4. He (saw, seen) a film about the rain forest that inspired him.

5. His teacher (had spoke, had spoken) highly of the film.

6. John (know, knew) quite a bit about the rain forest anyway.

7. He (had wrote, had written) a first draft for his poem.

8. The ending (gave, given) him quite a bit of trouble.

9. He (had went, had gone) to the contest expecting very little.

10. He (was, has been) surprised by the award.

Write It!   Imagine that you have won an award for something that you wrote or accomplished. Write an acceptance speech. Be sure to use the correct forms of irregular verbs in your speech.

Macmillan/McGraw-Hill

VERB PHRASES

> • A **verb phrase** consists of a main verb and all of its helping verbs.
>
> • A **helping verb** helps the main verb to show an action or make a statement.

When you write, keep in mind that your verbs, and verb phrases, must agree with their subjects.

         main helping

Dr. Jones *was working* in the South Pacific.

His helper *can dive* to great ocean depths.

Try It!   Draw one line under the main verb. Draw two lines under the helping verb.

1. His assistant has studied the South Pacific for years.

2. She has wondered about the tides her whole life.

3. She has photographed exotic creatures for decades.

4. Dr. Jones has invented a game about sea life.

5. Several of my friends were playing it recently.

6. Sam and June have mastered the game already.

7. Dr. Jones and his assistant were playing it with us.

8. They can answer all of the questions about sea life.

9. They will explain everything about the area.

10. The South Pacific has intrigued them, and they have created a game because of their interest in it.

Write It!   Imagine that you are editor of your school newspaper and that you have to write an article about a recent event at school. Write one or two paragraphs about the event. Identify verb phrases and helping verbs in your work.

PRESENT AND PAST PROGRESSIVE VERB FORMS

> - The **present progressive** form of a verb expresses action that is continuing now.
> - The **past progressive** form of a verb expresses action that continued for some time in the past.
> - Progressive forms are made up of a form of *be* and the present participle.

Be sure that you use the correct verb forms in you writing so that your reader will not be confused.

Present Progressive Form

I *am singing*

She *is singing.*

They *are singing.*

Past Progressive Form

I *was singing.*

She *was singing.*

They *were singing.*

Try It! Underline the verb phrase in each sentence. Tell whether it is *present progressive* or *past progressive*.

1. The movie theater is showing the latest adventure film.   _____

2. The theater is presenting the first 100 customers with free popcorn.   _____

3. Several groups were viewing the film yesterday.   _____

4. The owner was expecting a much smaller turn-out.   _____

5. The young stars are attracting a lot of attention.   _____

6. The film critic was explaining the plot to several people.   _____

7. I am planning another visit to this theater.   _____

8. I am looking forward to my next viewing.   _____

9. Many people are leaving the theater now.   _____

10. I am going inside the theater again right now.   _____

Write It! Write a paragraph that summarizes a movie you have recently seen. Give your opinion of the movie. Use and identify present and past progressive forms in your summary.

Macmillan/McGraw-Hill

PERFECT TENSES

> - The **present perfect tense** of a verb expresses an action that happened at an indefinite time in the past or that started in the past and is still happening in the present.
> - The **past perfect tense** expresses an action that was completed before another past action.
> - The **future perfect tense** expresses an action that will be completed in the future before some other future event.

When you write, make sure that you use the correct verb tenses so that your reader will understand the time order of your writing.

John *has collected* films about figure skating for years.   **present perfect**

He *had collected* them before he learned to skate.   **past perfect**

He *will have collected* 50 before next autumn.   **future perfect**

Try It!   Underline the verb in each sentence and tell its tense.

1. Larry has followed the career of that famous skater.   _____

2. Skating has fascinated him since his childhood.   _____

3. He had learned about skating by the age of five.   _____

4. Larry has revealed a real talent for figure skating himself.   _____

5. By graduation, Larry will have performed in several competitions.   _____

6. He has collected hundreds of videos of all the greats.   _____

7. Larry has studied their special moves.   _____

8. He had watched over 200 hours of tapes before his first

   competition.   _____

9. No wonder he will have completed so many hours on the ice.   _____

10. Larry has recognized his own talent at last.   _____

Write It!   Write a biography of someone you admire. Perhaps it is someone in the entertainment or sports field. Identify the perfect tense verbs in your work.

Macmillan/McGraw-Hill

PRONOUNS

- A **pronoun** takes the place of one or more nouns and the words that go with them.
- Use a **subject pronoun** as the subject of a sentence. Use an **object pronoun** as the object of a verb or a preposition.

Use personal pronouns in your writing to take the place of nouns so that you do not repeat nouns over and over again.

The *boys* stood on the pier.   *They* were fishing.

That *girl* is very funny.   *She* tells lots of jokes and stories.

Give the book to *Jim*.   I will give the book to *him*.

Try It! Underline the pronoun in each sentence.

1. Abraham Lincoln has always fascinated me.

2. He was President during a difficult time.

3. Southerners did not agree with him very much.

4. They thought he did not understand the situation in the South.

5. Nonetheless, he fought for what he believed in.

6. Susan wrote a report on him for history class.

7. She pointed out many things that I did not know about him.

8. She mentioned that he suffered from great sadness.

9. He must have felt very alone when people disagreed with him.

10. I believe he was very brave.

Write It! Write a report about the Civil War in this country. In your report consider some of the great generals on both sides. Share your report with a friend. Ask your friend to identify the personal pronouns.

Macmillan/McGraw-Hill

SUBJECT AND OBJECT PRONOUNS

> - Use a **subject pronoun** as the subject of a sentence.
> - Use an **object pronoun** as the object of a verb or preposition.

When you write, be sure to use subject and object pronouns correctly.

Subject Pronouns		Object Pronouns	
Singular	**Plural**	**Singular**	**Plural**
I	we	me	us
you	you	you	you
he, she, it	they	him, her, it	them

Try It! Draw one line under each pronoun. Tell whether the pronoun is a *subject pronoun* or an *object pronoun*.

1. I will attend the concert with Josie and Frank. _____

2. They will get the tickets at the box office. _____

3. Frank will pay me for the tickets. _____

4. I hope that Josie will go to dinner with us. _____

5. Please tell them the name of the restaurant. _____

6. They will hold the reservation for us. _____

7. Josie told him where to meet us. _____

8. You can come with her to the concert. _____

9. The concert promises to be fun for us. _____

10. I can't wait to see it. _____

Write It! Write a review of a concert that you attended. Who played at the concert? How did you like it? Give your opinion of the concert. Identify the subject and object pronouns in your review.

PRONOUN-ANTECEDENT AGREEMENT

> - An **antecedent** is a word or group of words to which a pronoun refers.
> - A pronoun must always agree with its antecedent in number and in gender.

When you write, make sure that your pronouns agree with their antecedents so that your readers will not be confused.

Antecedents

The battle was lost.

General Custer was defeated.

Pronouns

It was over in minutes.

He lost the battle.

Try It!   Draw one line under the pronoun. Draw two lines under its antecedent.

1. Sue loves American history. She is fascinated by the battles.

2. Wars have played a large part in U.S. history. They have been turning points for events that occurred later.

3. The Battle of The Alamo was significant. It paved the way for Texan independence from Mexico.

4. Mr. Jones is the history teacher. He makes history come alive.

5. Have the students heard of the Battle of San Jacinto? Mr. Jones says it was an important battle.

6. Sam Houston fought in the Battle of San Jacinto. He became a hero.

7. Santa Anna was the leader of the Mexican army. Santa Anna led it to many victories.

8. History is a fascinating subject. It is a subject full of interesting facts and details.

9. Sue may be a history teacher. She would make a very good teacher.

10. Sue would make the subject interesting for the students. Sue would make history come alive for them.

Write It!   What is your favorite school subject? Write a paragraph about your favorite subject. Identify the pronouns and antecedents.

Macmillan/McGraw-Hill

Book of Minilessons, Grades 6–8
Skill

INDEFINITE PRONOUNS

- An **indefinite pronoun** does not refer to a particular person, place, or thing.
- Any possessive pronoun *(hers, his, ours, mine)* used with an indefinite pronoun must agree with it in number and gender.

When you write make sure that you use indefinite pronouns correctly. Your textbook will have a complete list of indefinite pronouns.

Indefinite Pronouns

Singular: *another, each, everything, nobody, someone, somebody*

Plural: *both, few, many, others, several*

Singular or Plural: *all, any, most, none, some*

Try It!   Draw one line under each indefinite pronoun. Tell whether it is singular or plural.

1. Most of the bulbs blew out.   _____

2. One of ours did, too.   _____

3. All of us sat in the dark and wondered what to do.   _____

4. Some of the people looked very nervous.   _____

5. Others looked calm, but I knew they were worried.   _____

6. Most of the guests had left a long time ago.   _____

7. Each person was lost in his or her thoughts.   _____

8. Several of the people went to look for more light bulbs.   _____

9. None of them looked too optimistic.   _____

10. Nobody in the large, dark room moved until the light went on.   _____

Write It!   Has anything unexpected ever happened to you? Write a story about that time. Share your story with a friend. Have your friend identify the indefinite pronouns.

Name: _____   Date: _____

POSSESSIVE PRONOUNS

> • A **possessive pronoun** shows who or what owns something.
>
> • Possessive pronouns can come before a noun or stand alone.
>
> • Possessive pronouns never have apostrophes.

Remember that possessive pronouns do not have apostrophes. When you write, make sure to use possessive pronouns correctly.

Janet's speech was excellent. *Her speech* was excellent. *Hers* was the best.

Try It!   Draw a line under the possessive pronoun in each sentence. Tell whether it comes before the noun or stands alone.

1. My report is about Mother Jones.   _____

2. Her goal was to get better working conditions for laborers.   _____

3. Hers was a life of hard work and danger.   _____

4. A victim of oppression in Ireland, she fought its evil effects.   _____

5. Eugene V. Debs was a friend of hers.   _____

6. His work in organizing labor unions helped Mother Jones.   _____

7. The coal miners of West Virginia welcomed her help.   _____

8. Our country benefited from the work of Mother Jones.   _____

9. Working conditions were improved for her supporters.   _____

10. Perhaps the lives of your ancestors were improved, too.   _____

Write It!   Do you have a hero or heroine? Is it someone who helped the poor or disadvantaged? Write a report about your hero or heroine. Identify any possessive pronouns in your report.

CONTRACTIONS

> • A **contraction** is a word made by combining two words into one by leaving out one or more letters.

You can make your writing more informal when you use contractions. Be sure to punctuate contractions by using apostrophes correctly.

I will go to the party.   *I'll* go to the party.

I am excited about it.   *I'm* excited about it.

Try It! Underline the contraction in each sentence. Then write the words from which the contraction is formed.

1. I'll see all my friends at the party for Stella. _____

2. She'll certainly be surprised by the party. _____

3. We've kept the secret very well. _____

4. I know she's going to scream when she sees us. _____

5. Can you imagine how we'll feel when the day finally comes? _____

6. I'm sure we will not know what to do with ourselves in the morning. _____

7. They've been blowing up balloons for hours. _____

8. Are we sure he's not going to tell her? _____

9. Who'll be the first to yell "surprise"? _____

10. I bet it'll be Jay. _____

Write It! Write a dialog between two friends who are planning a surprise party for another friend. Be sure to use contractions correctly.

WHOSE, WHO, WHOM

> - An **interrogative pronoun** is a pronoun that introduces an interrogative sentence. *Whose, who,* and *whom* are interrogative pronouns.
> - Use *who* as the subject of a sentence. Use *whom* as the object of a verb or the object of a preposition.

When you write, be sure to use interrogative pronouns correctly. Do not confuse the pronoun *whose* with the contraction *who's* (*who is*).

   Who owns the new car?   To *whom* does the car belong?   *Whose* car is this?

Try It!   Underline the correct pronoun in parentheses.

1. (Who, Whom) invented the first car?

2. To (who, whom) can we give credit?

3. (Whose, Who's) idea was the assembly line?

4. For (who, whom) was the first car created?

5. (Who, Whom) best represents the inventor?

6. From (who, whom) did the plans come?

7. With (who, whom) did Ford work on his plans?

8. (Whose, Who's) financing made the first factory possible?

9. (Who, Whom) did Ford name as his successor?

10. (Whose, Who's) goals were met with the first inexpensive car?

Write It!   Imagine that you will interview a person whose achievements have changed the world. Write a series of questions that you would ask in the interview. Ask a classmate to check your work for correct use of *who, whom,* and *whose.*

Macmillan/McGraw-Hill

INTERROGATIVE AND DEMONSTRATIVE PRONOUNS

- An **interrogative pronoun** is a pronoun that introduces an interrogative sentence.

- A **demonstrative pronoun** points out something and stands alone in a sentence.

When you write, do not confuse *who's* (a contraction for *who is*) with the interrogative pronoun *whose*.

Interrogative Pronouns		Demonstrative Pronouns	
who	whose	this	that
whom	which	these	those
what			

Try It!   Underline the correct word in parentheses. Tell whether it is an interrogative pronoun, a contraction, or a demonstrative pronoun.

1. (Who , Whom) are the experts on American pop music?   _____

2. (Whose, Who's) CD player is that?   _____

3. (Whose, Who's) going to the concert with me?   _____

4. (That, What) is a very nice oboe.   _____

5. (This, These) are excellent seats.   _____

6. For (whom, who) are you saving those seats?   _____

7. (Which, That) singer is the best I've ever heard.   _____

8. (What, That) is that loud noise coming from backstage?   _____

9. (That, Who) is my good friend the guitar player.   _____

10. With (whom, who) are you attending the next concert?   _____

Write It!   Imagine that you are persuading someone to attend a concert with you. What reasons would you use? Write a persuasive paragraph. Use interrogative and demonstrative pronouns in your work.

Macmillan/McGraw-Hill

Book of Minilessons, Grades 6–8
Skill   #

REFLEXIVE AND INTENSIVE PRONOUNS

> - A **reflexive pronoun** directs the action of the verb to the subject.
> - An **intensive pronoun** adds emphasis to a noun or pronoun already named.

When you write, you can use reflexive pronouns to intensify a statement. Then the pronoun is an intensive pronoun.

Reflexive Pronouns

Singular	Plural
myself	ourselves
yourself	yourselves
himself, herself, itself	themselves

She reminded *herself* of the curfew. **reflexive**

She *herself* was not interested in the magazine. **intensive**

Try It! Draw one line under each reflexive or intensive pronoun. Then label each as *reflexive* or *intensive*.

1. I myself am not going to the party. _____

2. You can go by yourselves if you wish. _____

3. Tell him to let himself into the basement. _____

4. Since they do not want to go, we will be by ourselves. _____

5. They themselves are not happy about the situation. _____

6. Will they tell her themselves? _____

7. He himself is the host for the party. _____

8. The basement itself is huge enough for a party. _____

9. Will she allow herself one dance with anyone? _____

10. I feel sorry for him sitting in the corner by himself. _____

Write It! Write a description of someone you know. Use reflexive and intensive pronouns in your work.

ADJECTIVES

> • An **adjective** modifies or describes a noun or a pronoun.
>
> • A **predicate adjective** follows a linking verb and describes the subject.
>
> • A **participle** is a verb form that can be used as an adjective.

When you write, use colorful adjectives so that your writing will be descriptive.

This is *steamy* weather for May.   **adjective**

The weather was *humid*.   **predicate adjective**

The *exciting* weather report kept us awake.   **participle**

Try It!   Underline the adjectives, including participles. Identify the noun or pronoun the adjectives modify.

1. Sunny Florida was hot and sticky. _____

2. Interested tourists strolled through the parks. _____

3. Lazy turtles sunned themselves in metal cages. _____

4. The young children went on a guided tour. _____

5. The huge, sleek whales leaped in the air. _____

6. The whales were black and white. _____

7. Did you see that fabulous show? _____

8. The car was in the last row of the lot. _____

9. We were tired and weary at the end of the day. _____

10. The air-conditioned car felt good. _____

Write It!   Describe a trip that you have taken. What did you see? Where did you go? Share your description with a friend. Have your friend identify the adjectives in your description.

Macmillan/McGraw-Hill

ARTICLES AND PROPER ADJECTIVES

> • **Articles** are special kinds of adjectives. *The* is a **definite article**. *A* and *an* are **indefinite articles**.
>
> • A **proper adjective** is formed from a proper noun and begins with a capital letter.

Be sure to capitalize proper adjectives. Remember to use *an* before a noun that begins with a vowel and *a* before a noun that begins with a consonant.

an excellent *Italian* movie   *the German* musician   *a Spanish* aristocrat

Try It!   Draw one line under each proper adjective and rewrite it, capitalized. Draw two lines under each definite or indefinite article.

1. At the Food Fair we had many kinds of food and entertainment.   _____

2. Mrs. Russo brought her italian sausages.   _____

3. My mom supplied mexican tacos and all the trimmings.   _____

4. A sixth-grade class made greek salads.   _____

5. The hungarian polkas had everyone on the dance floor.   _____

6. An excited polish woman danced and danced.   _____

7. Someone donated an entire box of florida oranges.   _____

8. The Kellys brought irish stew and soda bread.   _____

9. The only thing missing was chinese food.   _____

10. Next year we intend to have an english tea party.   _____

Write It!   Think of all the foods that originated in other countries. Write a short report about foods that come from around the world. Identify all the articles and proper adjectives in your report.

COMPARATIVE ADJECTIVES

> - The **comparative form** of an adjective compares two nouns. Add *er* to many adjectives to form the comparative.
> - Use the word *more* to form the comparative of some two-syllable and all three-syllable adjectives.

Do not use *more* with an adjective that ends in *er*.

Adjective	Comparative
tall	taller
active	more active
fascinating	more fascinating

Try It!   Underline the correct comparative form in parentheses.

1. In my opinion, London is (interestinger, more interesting) than Paris.

2. Is Big Ben (taller, more tall) than the Eiffel Tower?

3. The Tate Gallery is (more smaller, smaller) than the Louvre.

4. Nonetheless, shopping is (more fun, funner) in Paris.

5. The art is (most accessible, more accessible) in the Tate.

6. But the Tate is (gloomier, more gloomy) than the Louvre.

7. Still, the Louvre is (grander, more grand) in many ways.

8. London's West End is (popularer, more popular) than the Paris Opera.

9. The sculpture in Paris is (more stirring, most stirring) than the sculpture in London.

10. I think the Paris subway is (nicer, more nice) than the London subway.

Write It!   Write a descriptive paragraph comparing two places that you like. Then, exchange papers with a classmate and have your classmate make sure that you have used comparative adjectives correctly.

Macmillan/McGraw-Hill

SUPERLATIVE ADJECTIVES

> - The **superlative** form of an adjective compares more than two nouns. Add *est* to many adjectives to form the superlative.
> - Add the word *most* to form the superlative of some two-syllable adjectives and all three-syllable adjectives.

Do not use *most* with an adjective that ends in *est*.

Adjective	Superlative
tall	tallest
active	most active
fascinating	most fascinating

Try It!   Underline the correct superlative form in parentheses.

1. That was the (more accomplished, most accomplished) pianist I have ever heard.

2. The guests were (most impressed, more impressed) with him of all the performers.

3. The reviewers were (most kindest, kindest) to the soprano.

4. She had the (best, bestest) voice I ever heard.

5. The tenor had the (most sweetest, sweetest) quality.

6. I thought this recital was the (more varied, most varied) of all I have attended.

7. In your view, who had the (more interesting, most interesting) solo?

8. I thought the flute player was the (engagingest, most engaging).

9. She had the (prettiest, most pretty) gown.

10. She played for the (longest, most longest) time.

Write It!   What is your favorite kind of music? Write a paragraph that explains why. Make sure that you have used superlative adjectives correctly in your paragraph.

DEMONSTRATIVE ADJECTIVES

> • A **demonstrative adjective** points out something and describes a noun by answering the question *which one?* or *which ones?*
>
> • A **demonstrative pronoun** points out a specific person, place, or thing and stands alone in a sentence.

When you write, be sure to use *this* and *these* to point out nearby people, places, and things and to use *that* and *those* to point out people, places, and things that are farther away.

Demonstrative Adjectives: *This* book is fiction. *Those* books are old.

Demonstrative Pronouns: *This* is mine. *Those* are not for sale.

Try It! Draw one line under each demonstrative adjective and two lines under each demonstrative pronoun.

1. This library is over 100 years old.

2. That collection was given to the library last year.

3. Many of those books are first editions.

4. Have you ever seen one of those.

5. These are just beautiful leather bindings.

6. That first edition was signed by the author.

7. Is this book really 75 years old?

8. These books are antique children's books.

9. Look at these colorful illustrations!

10. That part of the library is being painted.

Write It! Work with a partner to write a travel brochure describing a landmark in your city or town. Check your work to make sure you have used demonstrative adjectives and pronouns correctly.

Macmillan/McGraw-Hill

ADVERBS

> • An **adverb** is a word that modifies a verb, an adjective, or another adverb.
>
> • Adverbs answer the questions *how? when? where?* and to *what extent?*

When you write, use adverbs to add clarity and detail to your writing.

The horse ran *quickly*. **how**   The spectators cheered *first*. **when**

The race is held *here*. **where**   That was *very* fast. **to what extent**

Try It!   Draw one line under each adverb. Draw two lines under the word it modifies.

1. The favorite in the race was very young.

2. She had run yesterday and was extremely fast.

3. Everyone eagerly watched the horses parade around the ring.

4. The young horse appeared last in the parade.

5. Today she would win her biggest competition.

6. Would she run surely and quickly?

7. The crowd was quite impressed with the rider.

8. He smiled happily at the crowds.

9. The horses' coats shone brightly in the sunlight.

10. The race would end triumphantly for the young horse.

Write It!   Imagine that you are a reporter at a sports event. In a paragraph, describe the event for a radio broadcast. Exchange paragraphs with a classmate. Identify the adverbs.

Macmillan/McGraw-Hill

COMPARATIVE ADVERBS

- The **comparative form** of an adverb compares two actions. Add *er* or use the word *more* with the adverb.
- Do not use *more* with *er*.

When you write, be sure to use the comparative form correctly. Use *more* with most two-syllable and three-syllable words.

Adverb	Comparative
far	farther
strongly	more strongly

Try It!   Underline the correct form of the comparative adverb in parentheses.

1. The hurricane winds blew (more strongly, most stronger) today than yesterday.

2. The sky turned dark (earlier, more earlier) in the day.

3. The rain fell (harder, more hard) than it did yesterday.

4. The waves in the ocean crashed (more wildly, wildlier) than they had earlier.

5. Did the rain fall (more heavily, most heavily) today or yesterday?

6. I think the wind gusted (more severely, most severely) yesterday than it did today.

7. This hurricane traveled (farther, more farther) up the coast

8. The traffic was moving (slowlyer, more slowly) than it was earlier.

9. Electricity was affected (more seriously, most seriously) this time.

10. Are these storms occurring (most frequently, more frequently) than they did before?

Write It!   Compare storms that occur in different parts of the country. Write two paragraphs. Then, check your paragraphs for correct use of comparative adverbs.

Book of Minilessons, Grades 6–8
Skill #

Macmillan/McGraw-Hill

SUPERLATIVE ADVERBS

> • The **superlative form** of an adverb compares more than two actions. Add *est* or use the word *most* with the adverb.
>
> • Do not use *est* with *most*.

Be sure to use the superlative form of an adverb correctly in your writing.

Adverb	**Superlative**
far	farthest
strongly	most strongly

Try It!   Draw one line under the superlative form of an adverb.

1. Our drama club performed the scene most forcefully of all the groups.

2. The actor performing most daringly of all was a sixth grader.

3. He dressed the most elegantly also.

4. Do they perform comedies most frequently?

5. The sixth-grade performers acted most confidently of all.

6. In the musicals, the seventh graders sang the most beautifully.

7. One drama required the fastest costume change ever.

8. The play was so long, they had the most intermissions ever.

9. The parents were the most excited people in the audience.

10. The ushers behaved the most nervously of all.

Write It!   Write a paragraph about your favorite movie or play. Share your paragraph with a friend. Ask your friend to identify superlative adverbs in your work.

Name: _____   Date: _____

ADJECTIVES AND ADVERBS

> - Use **adjectives**, including *bad, good,* and *real,* to describe nouns and pronouns.
> - Use **adverbs**, including *badly, well,* and *really,* to modify verbs, adjectives, and other adverbs.
> - You can also use *well* as an adjective when referring to someone's health.

When you write, be sure to use adjectives and adverbs correctly.

The *happy* camper lighted the fire.   **adjective**

The camper sang *happily* by the fire.   **adverb**

The camper saw a *real* cowhand.   **adjective**

He was *really* impressed.   **adverb**

Try It!   Draw one line under each adjective. Draw two lines under each adverb.

1. The camper plodded slowly up the crooked path.

2. The black horse limped badly.

3. It had a bad sprain in its left front leg.

4. The unhappy camper did not think the horse looked well.

5. Everyone had told the camper to avoid the dangerous pass.

6. He had proudly ignored everyone's advice.

7. Now he was in a real mess.

8. He had really goofed by not paying attention.

9. Would anyone find the lonely camper and the injured horse?

10. Suddenly, he heard good news on his short-wave radio.

Write It!   Write a description of a difficulty you once found yourself in. Share your description with a friend. Ask your friend to identify the adjectives and adverbs in your work.

DOUBLE NEGATIVES

> - A **double negative** is the incorrect use of two negative words to convey a negative meaning.
> - Avoid double negatives by using only one negative word to convey a negative meaning.

In your writing, if you use *not* in a sentence, be sure that you do not use another negative word in that sentence. Remember that some contractions have the word *not* in them.

Incorrect: The highwire artist *did not use no net.*

Correct: The highwire artist *did not use a net.*

Correct: The highwire artist *used no net.*

Try It!   Chose the correct word in parentheses.

1. The circus (has, hasn't) hardly been in town a week.

2. The admission fee (is, isn't) nothing to worry about.

3. Nobody (never, ever) has to stand in line for long.

4. You won't see such talented acts (anywhere, nowhere).

5. There (was, wasn't) hardly room for another person in the audience.

6. No one had (never, ever) seen such acts!

7. The spotlight didn't shine on (anyone, no one) but the lion tamer.

8. During his act there (was, wasn't) hardly a sound in the tent.

9. There wasn't (any, no) talking or whispering.

10. Hardly (no one, anyone) left during the intermission.

Write It!   What if you participated in an event in which everything went wrong? Write a paragraph about the experience. Check to make sure that you have used no double negatives.

MISPLACED MODIFIERS

> - A **modifier** can be a single adjective or adverb, or it can be a phrase, such as a prepositional phrase.
> - A modifier should be as close as possible to the word it modifies. A **misplaced modifier** can result in a confusing or misleading sentence.

When you write, be sure that your modifiers add meaning to the words they describe.

Correct: The boy was running *wildly* and almost lost his shoe.

Incorrect: Running *wildly*, the shoes were almost lost.

Correct: The girl *in the blue jacket* saw the robbery.

Incorrect: The girl saw the robbery *in the blue jacket*.

Try It!   Underline the misplaced modifiers in the sentences. If the modifier is not misplaced, write **C** next to the sentence.

1. The woman at the checkout stand was alert. _____

2. Alert as ever, the robber was sighted by the guard. _____

3. The robber confronted the guard with a mask over his face . _____

4. The woman with her hand on the counter paused. _____

5. She brought her hand to the alarm that connected to the police station slowly . _____

6. With her hand on the alarm, she had second thoughts. _____

7. Was the man in the funny clothes really a robber? _____

9. The guard stood looking at the robber shouting "Halt!" _____

10. Decisively, she finally pushed the alarm. _____

Write It!   Have you ever had to make a quick decision? Write a paragraph telling about that time. How did you reach your decision? Check your work to see that you do not have any misplaced modifiers.

PREPOSITIONS

> • A **preposition** relates a noun or pronoun to another word in a sentence.
>
> • A **prepositional phrase** is a group of words that begins with a preposition and ends with a noun or a pronoun. That noun or pronoun is called the **object of the preposition**.

When you write, you can use prepositional phrases to describe locations.

The boy looked *under the bed*.   Check *inside the trunk*.

The book bag was *on the table*.   The car is *behind the house*.

Try It!   Draw one line under the prepositional phrase. Draw two lines under the object of the preposition.

1. Jason has misplaced his book bag somewhere in the house.

2. He misplaced it sometime after dinner.

3. Is it wedged behind the big bookcase in the hall?

4. I saw him put it on the bookcase.

5. Perhaps he left it outside the house.

6. No, I'm sure it is inside this house.

7. In the meantime, put the books into this briefcase.

8. I will lose my papers among all these books.

9. That report by my sister is very good.

10. I have been upset about this since last night.

Write It!   Think of something that you once misplaced. How did you go about finding it? Write a paragraph that tells about this event. Identify the prepositional phrases in your work.

USING PRONOUNS IN PREPOSITIONAL PHRASES

> • When the object of a preposition is a pronoun, use an object pronoun.
>
> • Use *me* or *us* last in a compound object of a preposition.
>
> • Do not use a reflexive pronoun when an object pronoun is needed.

When you write, be sure to use object pronouns as objects of prepositions.

Correct: Have you sent the letter to *me*?

Correct: Except for *Bill and me,* no one received the mailing.

Incorrect: Except for me and Bill, no one received the mailing.

Correct: This will not come between *Bill and me.*

Incorrect: This will not come between Bill and myself.

Try It!   Underline the correct word or words in parentheses.

1. The glee club sent out a mailing to (us, ourselves).

2. They sent one to (me and Tom, Tom and me).

3. For (Sara and her, her and Sara) they made an exception.

3. Give that sheet music to (he and Tom, Tom and him).

4. Except for (she, her), no one is interested in joining.

5. Between (us, we), I think the club will not survive.

6. We can't keep it going between (us, ourselves).

7. She talked with (my sister and me, me and my sister) about the club.

8. They received donations from (him and I, him and me).

9. She will save the music for (us, ourselves).

10. I hope they give the music stands to (us, we).

Write It!   What if you had to raise money for a school club? How would you go about it? Write a paragraph explaining what you would do. Share your paragraph with a classmate. Have your classmate check that you have used the correct pronouns in prepositional phrases.

PREPOSITIONAL PHRASES AS ADJECTIVES AND ADVERBS

> • An **adjective phrase** is a prepositional phrase that modifies a noun or a pronoun.
> • An **adverb phrase** is a prepositional phrase that may modify a verb.
> • An adverb phrase can tell *when, where,* or *why* an action takes place.

When you write, you can use adjective and adverb phrases to add description to your work.

The trees *by the river* are lovely.   **adjective phrase**

Sally went *to the state park*.   **adverb phrase, where?**

She hiked *until sunset*.   **adverb phrase, when?**

The guide asked *about her route*.   **adverb phrase, why?**

Try It!   Draw one line under each adjective phrase. Draw two lines under each adverb phrase.

1. The hiker in the blue shorts was very good.

2. She walked toward the trail quickly.

3. The trail wound through a deep forest.

4. The forest with the huge trees did not frighten her.

5. She hiked over the rough trail easily.

6. She paused at a clearing.

7. A guide for the park service appeared suddenly.

8. The guide pointed to a large group of trees.

9. She looked into the darkness.

10. Behind the tree stood a deer with a speckled tail.

Write It!   Write a story about an adventure you have had or would like to have. Be sure to use prepositional phrases to describe the setting of your adventure and some of the events. Share your story with a friend. Ask your friend to identify the adjective and adverb phrases.

Macmillan/McGraw-Hill

Book of Minilessons, Grades 6–8
Skill

CONJUNCTIONS

- A **coordinating conjunction** connects parts of a sentence or two sentences.
- **Correlative conjunctions** are pairs of words such as *neither/nor* used to connect parts of a sentence or two sentences.
- A **subordinating conjunction** is used to introduce a subordinate clause.

When you write, you add variety to your work by using compound and complex sentences. Be sure to use conjunctions correctly in these sentences.

Bob *and* Joe studied the Vikings.   **coordinating**

The Vikings were fine sailors, *and* they were the first to arrive here.   **coordinating**

Neither Joe *nor* Bob had known much about the Vikings.   **correlative**

After they studied the Vikings, they knew more.   **subordinating**

Try It!   Draw one line under the coordinating conjunctions. Draw two lines under the correlative conjunctions. Write any subordinating conjunctions after the sentence.

1. If the Vikings really landed first, it is quite some story.   _____

2. There is little physical evidence, and historians disagree about it.   _____

3. Either Bob or Joe will make a report on their findings.   _____

4. The Vikings arrived before Columbus did.   _____

5. They must have landed in New England if they found grapes there.   _____

6. They built shelters and scouted the area.   _____

7. Neither the Vikings nor the Indians made headway with an alliance.   _____

8. They wanted to be friendly, but circumstances prevented it.   _____

9. Whenever the weather permitted, the Vikings explored the land.   _____

10. Bob believes the evidence, but Joe is still unsure.   _____

Write It!   Write a report about the Vikings. Share your report with a friend. Ask your friend to identify the conjunctions in your report.

Book of Minilessons, Grades 6–8
Skill

Macmillan/McGraw-Hill

MAKING VERBS AGREE WITH COMPOUND SUBJECTS

> • When two or more subjects are joined by *and* or *both . . . and,* the verb is plural.
>
> • When two or more subjects are joined by *or, nor, either . . . or,* or *neither . . . nor,* the verb agrees with the subject that is closest to it.

Remember that a compound subject can be three words.

Tom, Sara, and Joyce *are* in the debate club.

Both Tom and Sara *have been* members for years.

Tom or last year's winner *is* the one to watch.

Neither Sara nor the other winners *worry* Tom.

Try It!   Draw one line under the correct form of the verb in parentheses. Draw two lines under the conjunctions.

1. Either Tom or Sara (call, calls) the debate club meeting to order.

2. Beth and I (love, loves) the debate club.

3. A debate or good argument always (intrigue, intrigues) us.

4. Both Tom and Sara (helps, help) to set the agenda for the meeting.

5. This month neither Tom nor Sara (have, has) the time.

6. Therefore, Beth and I (have, has) to do it.

7. Beth or the other members (choose, chooses) the topics.

8. Both Alison and I (ask, asks) for silence.

9. The schoolroom or the auditorium (is, are) a good location for the debate.

10. The principal and three teachers (is, are) the judges.

Write It!   Think of an issue that interests you and would be a good debate topic. Write some pros and cons for the issue. If you include any compound subjects in your writing, make sure that your verbs agree with them.

Macmillan/McGraw-Hill

INTERJECTIONS

> - An **interjection** is a word or phrase used to express strong feeling.
> - Use an exclamation mark after an interjection that stands alone. Use a comma after an interjection that comes at the beginning of a sentence.

The use of interjections can add expression to a character's dialog. Be sure to punctuate interjections correctly.

Common Interjections: *Wow, Ah, Aha, Hooray, Gee, Gosh, Oh, my, Oops*

Wow! Did you see those fireworks?

Wow, the fireworks were spectacular this year.

Try It!   Underline the interjection in each sentence.

1. Aha! I knew the fireworks would surprise you.

2. I knew just what your reaction would be. Wow!

3. Hey, I saw you here last year on the Fourth of July.

4. Oh, no , that was two years ago.

5. Oops , I almost spilled my soft drink.

6. Gee , I don't want to miss the finale.

7. Good heavens , look at that beautiful display!

8. The heavens are completely lighted. Hooray !

9. I have never seen anything like it. Gee!

10. Wow , I hope this celebration never ends.

Write It!   Get ready for a Fourth of July celebration by designing a poster. Identify any interjections that you use.

Macmillan/McGraw-Hill

SENTENCES AND CLAUSES

- A **simple sentence** has one complete subject and one complete predicate.
- A **compound sentence** has two or more independent clauses that can stand alone as a sentence.
- A **subordinate clause** is a group of words that has a subject and a predicate, but cannot stand alone as a complete sentence.
- A **complex sentence** contains an independent clause and one or more subordinate clauses.

When you write, be sure to use a comma after a subordinate clause at the beginning of a complex sentence.

Simple: *Early explorers were brave.*

Compound: *They explored unknown lands, and they survived.*

Complex: *After they explored an area, they usually mapped it.*

Try It! Write *simple, compound,* or *complex* next to each sentence to tell which kind of sentence it is.

1. Thomas Jefferson asked Meriwether Lewis to lead an expedition. _____

2. The United States had purchased a large parcel of land from France, and it was completely unexplored. _____

3. Although Lewis wanted to go, he did not wish to go alone. _____

4. He asked his friend William Clark, an army officer, to go with him. _____

5. The expedition began its trip in St. Louis, Missouri. _____

6. When they set out, they knew their mission was to find a safe passage to the West. _____

7. They faced many hardships, but they did not give up. _____

8. The trip took 18 months to complete. _____

9. As the group looked at the Pacific Ocean, they were happy. _____

10. After they returned to Washington, they presented President Jefferson with many maps of the area. _____

Write It! Write a diary entry for one of the members of the expedition. Identify simple, compound, and complex sentences in the entry.

Macmillan/McGraw-Hill

  Book of Minilessons, Grades 6–8
Skill

ADJECTIVE CLAUSES

> • An **adjective clause** is a subordinate clause that modifies, or describes, a noun or pronoun in the independent clause of a complex sentence.
>
> • An adjective clause usually begins with a **relative pronoun** such as *who, whom, which,* or *that.*

When you write, be sure to use commas to set off an adjective clause that is not essential to the meaning of the sentence.

The people who created the sculpture were at the show.

The patrons, who are avid supporters, applauded the artists.

Try It!   Underline the adjective clause in each sentence. If the sentence needs commas, add them.

1. The show that opened recently included outstanding sculpture.

2. The pieces which were over six feet tall were impressive.

3. The artists who created the pieces worked in marble.

4. The marble which was imported from Italy was flawless.

5. The piece that was my favorite was an angel.

6. The owner of the gallery whom I met in college was pleased with the show.

7. The refreshments that were served at the reception were delicious.

8. Many of the people who came to the show purchased pieces.

9. The artists whose work was so well received beamed.

10. The angel that I liked is still available.

Write It!   What kind of art do you like? Write a description of a painting or a piece of sculpture that appeals to you. Exchange your writing with a classmate. Ask your classmate to identify adjective clauses.

Macmillan/McGraw-Hill

ADVERB CLAUSES

> • A **adverb clause** modifies the verb in the independent clause of a complex sentence.
>
> • An adverb clause usually begins with a **subordinating conjunction**, such as *because, when, although,* or *if.*

When you write, remember to place a comma after a clause that comes at the beginning of the sentence.

Although I was very tired, I continued to practice.

I shot several baskets before I went to bed.

Try It! Underline the adverb clause in each sentence. If a sentence needs a comma, add it.

1. Because the tournament is soon I am practicing every night.

2. If we win this tournament   we will go to the state competition.

3. The team plays well when it has practiced regularly .

4. I have been steadily improving ever since I began to practice more.

5. Although the coach still has doubts I know I am ready to start.

6. Before I go to school I practice.

7. I also practice when I come home from school.

8. I even practice before I go to bed.

9. If you see Coach Kelly tell him I am ready.

10. Perhaps he will come to his senses when he sees me play.

Write It! Write a letter to the editor that expresses your point of view about an issue that is important to you. Identify the adverb clauses in your letter.

Macmillan/McGraw-Hill

NOUN CLAUSES

> • A **noun clause** is a subordinate clause that functions as a noun.
>
> • A noun clause can be a subject, a direct object, a predicate noun, or an object of a preposition.
>
> • Some words that introduce noun clauses are *how, that, why, what, when, where, whose,* and *who.*

When you write, you can use noun clauses in the same ways that nouns are used.

Subject:	*How I learned to fly* is my essay topic.
Direct Object:	I will pursue *whatever aspect interests me.*
Object of a Preposition:	I will focus on *what I prefer.*
Predicate Noun:	The field is *where I spend my time.*

Try It!   Underline the noun clause in each sentence. Tell how it is used.

1. Why I love to fly is obvious.   _____

2. Whoever learns to fly observes many things.   _____

3. The view from the plane is what intrigues me.   _____

4. I will fly with whoever wants a ride.   _____

5. The flight plan gave me an idea about
   which route would be best.   _____

6. My only worry is how I will get there on time.   _____

7. Now I wonder which route I should take.   _____

8. The Grand Canyon is what I saw.   _____

9. What I really need is a better map.   _____

10. Which plane I take depends on the weather.   _____

Write It!   Write a paragraph about something you would like to learn to do. Identify the noun clauses in your work.

Macmillan/McGraw-Hill

PARTICIPLES AND PARTICIPIAL PHRASES

> • A **participle** is a verb form that can be used as an adjective to modify nouns or pronouns.
>
> • A **participial phrase** is a group of words that includes a participle used as an adjective and other words that complete the meaning.

Remember that the present participle is formed by adding *ing* to a verb and the past participle is formed by adding *ed*. In your writing, be sure to place a comma after a participial phrase that comes at the beginning of the sentence.

Racing to the bus stop, the woman tripped.   **participial phrase**

Embarrassed by her clumsiness, she frowned.   **participial phrase**

The *frowning* woman looked unhappy.   **participle**

Try It!   Draw one line under the participle or participial phrase. Draw two lines under the noun or pronoun that the phrase modifies.

1. The interested bystander asked if he could help.

2. An excited bus driver screeched the bus to a stop.

3. Waving him on, the woman sat on a bench.

4. Shrugging with disgust, the bystander boarded the bus.

5. The woman looked at her beautiful imported shoe.

6. Hoping that it wasn't ruined, the woman removed it.

7. Suddenly, a child dressed in a snowsuit appeared.

8. Staring at the woman, the child extended her hand.

9. Looking quite cute, the little girl made the woman feel better.

10. Standing up, the woman shook the little girl's hand.

Write It!   Write a story about an embarrassing incident. Share your story with a classmate. Have your classmate identify any participles or participial phrases in your writing.

Macmillan/McGraw-Hill

GERUNDS

> • A **gerund** is a verb form that ends in *ing* and is used as a noun.
>
> • A **gerund phrase** is a group of words that includes a gerund and other words that complete its meaning.

When you write, you can add variety to your sentences by using gerunds and gerund phrases as subjects and as direct objects.

Running is one of my favorite activities. **gerund as subject**

She chose *marathon running* as her event. **gerund phrase as direct object**

Try It!   Underline each gerund or gerund phrase. Tell whether it is a **subject** or a **direct object.**

1. Race walking is great fun. _____

2. Sprinting is my favorite event. _____

3. Training for the various events is difficult. _____

4. The instructor likes cheering for the racers. _____

5. Watching from the sidelines is fun too. _____

6. I dislike watching the race from there. _____

7. She enjoys winning more than anything else. _____

8. Finishing the race will be my biggest triumph. _____

9. Participating is all I care about. _____

10. My parents love rooting loudly for the racers. _____

Write It!   Write a comparison/contrast paragraph that explains the similarities and differences of two sports. Identify the gerunds and gerund phrases in your work.

Macmillan/McGraw-Hill

INFINITIVES

> • An **infinitive** is formed with the word *to* and the base form of the verb.
>
> • An **infinitive phrase** includes an infinitive and other words that complete its meaning.

You can use infinitives and infinitive phrases as subjects or direct objects in your sentences when you write.

    To sing is a glorious gift.   **infinitive-subject**

    We plan *to sing* at the concert.   **infinitive-direct object**

    We decided *to sing loudly* at the finale.   **infinitive phrase-direct object**

    I am going *to the concert*.   **prepositional phrase**

Try It!   Draw one line under infinitives and infinitive phrases. Draw two lines under prepositional phrases.

1. Sarah loves to dance.

2. She will go to great lengths for an opportunity.

3. Many people will go to Hayes Stadium for the concert.

4. To see all those people will be fantastic.

5. Thousands plan to attend.

6. To buy tickets may be a problem.

7. We rushed to the box office early.

8. I want to sit in the first row near the band.

9. Do you plan to watch every act?

10. They decided to arrive an hour early.

Write It!   What hobby do you like? Write a paragraph about your favorite hobby. Identify any infinitives or infinitive phrases in your work.

Macmillan/McGraw-Hill

END PUNCTUATION

> - End **declarative** and **imperative** sentences with a **period**.
> - End **interrogative** sentences with a **question mark**.
> - End **exclamatory** sentences with an **exclamation mark**.

When you write, be sure to punctuate your sentences correctly.

Declarative: *World War II began in Europe.*

Imperative: *Read the report about the battle.*

Interrogative: *Did you study the causes of the war?*

Exclamatory: *Good grief, the hardships must have been terrible!*

Try It!   Add the correct end punctuation to each of the sentences.

1. Germany committed several acts of aggression__

2. Was Hitler the leader of Germany then__

3. The rest of Europe was worried when Hitler marched into Czechoslovakia__

4. My heavens, Hitler was quite a tyrant__

5. France and Great Britain declared war on Germany__

6. What did the United States do__

7. Read your history book to find out__

8. The United States gave arms and supplies to Great Britain and France__

9. Did that help the war effort in Europe__

10. Goodness, the war years must have been terrible__

Write It!   What do you know about World War II? Conduct some research about World War II and write a short report about one aspect of the war. Be sure to use correct end punctuation in your report.

Macmillan/McGraw-Hill

Book of Minilessons, Grades 6–8
Skill #

COMMAS

> - Use **commas** before the conjunction in a compound sentence.
> - Use **commas** between the names of cities and states.
> - Use a **comma** to separate the day and the year in a date.
> - Use **commas** to separate words in a series.
> - Use **commas** after introductory words or phrases.
> - Use **commas** to set off words in direct address and appositives.

When you write, be sure to use commas after the state and after the year in sentences.

Sam is a good friend, and I spend a lot of time with him.

He lives in Tupelo, Mississippi, on a farm.

He was born on December 21, 1940, in Jackson.

Sam is smart, polite, and kind to me.

No, Sam, the nicest person in the world, does not have brothers or sisters.

You, my friend, will come to dinner when Sam is here.

Try It!   Add commas to the following sentences where they are needed.

1. The friends went to the movies and they saw a great comedy.

2. The plays were great in New York New York on Broadway.

3. We made reservations for March 11   1997 at the hotel.

4. We went to concerts saw plays and toured museums.

5. Sam will you please stop dancing in the aisles.

6. The usher a man in a green suit looked annoyed.

7. We can go to dinner but we don't have time for a play.

8. Sam will return to Jackson Mississippi on a jet.

9. He has only two more days here and then he will have to go home.

10. He will come to visit again on January 5 1998.

Write It!   Write a description of a day that you spent with a friend. What did you do? Where did you go? Be sure to use commas correctly in your writing.

Book of Minilessons, Grades 6–8
Skill

63

COLONS

> • Use a **colon** after the greeting in a business letter.
>
> • Use a **colon** to separate the hour and the minute when you write the time of day.
>
> • Use a **colon** to introduce a list of items that ends a sentence. Use a phrase such as *the following* or *as follows* before the list.

When you write, be sure to use colons correctly when you include lists in your work.

Dear Madam: 7:00 A.M.

Please bring the following: a toothbrush, toothpaste, and two towels.

Try It!   Add ten colons where they are needed to this letter.

July 16, 1996

Dear Sir

I am writing to complain about the treatment I have received from your company regarding an order. I called on Tuesday, December 6, at 9 00 A.M.
The message I left at that time was ignored. I called again at 3 00, and one of your assistants was very rude to me. Consequently, I am writing this letter.

Three weeks ago, I ordered the following a pup tent, two canteens, and a sleeping bag. The instructions I gave on my order were as follows ship the order overnight mail, pack it in one carton, and deliver it by 10 00 A.M.

That is not the way I received the order. It came three days later at 5 00 P.M. I was not at home so I had to go to the post office at 8 00 A.M. the next day.

At the post office, I was given the following information the package had been returned to you, and you had refused delivery. The package was lost somewhere in the system.

These are my instructions to you. Please proceed as follows return my money, tear up my order, and do not send me another catalog.

                                        Yours truly,

                                        An aggravated customer

Write It!   Write a business letter of your own. Be sure to use colons correctly.

Macmillan/McGraw-Hill

QUOTATION MARKS

> - Use **quotation marks** before and after a direct quotation.
> - Use **quotation marks** to identify the title of a short story, an essay, a song, a short poem, a book chapter, or a magazine or newspaper article.

Be sure to use end punctuation correctly when you write quotations.

"Please sit down," said the instructor.   "Who will take the roll?" he asked.

John said, "I hope you win the contest."   "Wow, what a speech!" she said.

"My Personal Quest"   "Hey Jude"   "The Necklace"

Try It!   Add quotation marks where they are needed to each of the following sentences.

1. Please enter the contest, encouraged the teacher.

2. My essay is called How I Spent the Best Day of My Life.

3. The writing contest is open to all, said the advisor.

4. What are you going to write about? asked Susan.

5. Jake is going to write about his favorite song, In the Good Old Summertime.

6. Who will read my poem? asked John.

7. Sam read The Gift of the Magi by O. Henry.

8. Did you enjoy it? asked Sylvia.

9. That magazine article is called The Way of the World.

10. Bring your poems to my office, said Sarah, before the end of the day.

Write It!   Write a short story about a real life adventure. Be sure to use quotation marks for any dialog that you write.

ITALICS/UNDERLINING

> • Use **italics** or **underlining** to identify the title of a book, a play, a film, a TV series, a magazine, or a newspaper.

Be sure to use italics or underlining correctly when you write reviews of books and films.

Book: *The Incredible Journey*	Magazine: *Time*
Newspaper: *Main Street Journal*	TV series: *Sesame Street*
Film: *Free Willy*	Play: *A Christmas Carol*

Try It!   Add underlining where it is needed to the following sentences.

1. Did you see the movie Little Women?

2. It was reviewed in the Washington Post.

3. I watch 60 Minutes every Sunday night.

4. Sally went to see Beauty and the Beast on Broadway.

5. Do you subscribe to Newsweek?

6. Marc Anderson appeared on Jeopardy last week.

7. I read Sarah, Plain and Tall last year.

8. They filmed Home Alone in my neighborhood.

9. Who was the star of Cats?

10. Entertainment Weekly had a review of that film.

Write It!   Write a review of a film, book, or play that you have seen recently. Be sure to use italics or underlining correctly in your review.

Macmillan/McGraw-Hill

APOSTROPHES

- Use an **apostrophe** and an *s* ('s) to form the possessive of a singular noun or a plural noun that does not end in *s*.
- Use an **apostrophe** alone to form the possessive of a plural noun that ends in *s*.
- Use an **apostrophe** and an *s* ('s) to form the possessive of an indefinite pronoun.
- Use an **apostrophe** in a contraction to show where letters have been omitted.

When you write, be sure to use apostrophes correctly in possessive nouns.

Dorrie's book   the children's room   the actors' roles

anybody's sweater   would + not = wouldn't

Try It!   Add apostrophes where they are needed in the following sentences.

1. The Andersons house is on my block.

2. They dont have a very big yard.

3. The childrens tree house is in the backyard.

4. Robs sand box is also back there.

5. The girls bikes are often found on the driveway.

6. Everybodys toys are in the toy box in the garage.

7. Mr. Anderson doesnt mind all the children.

8. His six brothers belongings were all over the house.

9. Is this someones jacket?

10. Dont throw that jacket away.

Write It!   Write a paragraph describing something that belongs to you. Share your paragraph with a classmate. Ask your classmate to identify where you have used apostrophes correctly.

ABBREVIATIONS

> - In both informal and formal writing you may use **abbreviations** for certain organizations and government agencies.
> - In informal writing and on envelopes, you may use United States Postal Service abbreviations for the names of the states.
> - In scientific writing use abbreviations for units of measure. The abbreviation is the same for the singular and plural units.

In most cases, when your writing is formal, you will not use abbreviations.

American Library Association	*ALA*
Alabama	*AL*
pound(s)	*lb*
kilometer(s)	*km*

Try It!   Write the abbreviations for the following.

1. California _____

2. Association for the Prevention of Cruelty to Animals _____

3. inch _____

4. meter _____

5. ounce _____

6. New York _____

7. Indiana _____

8. Federal Bureau of Investigation _____

9. Internal Revenue Service _____

10. Ohio _____

Write It!   Write a paragraph about a science subject that interests you. Be sure to write the correct abbreviations for any units of measure that you use.

Macmillan/McGraw-Hill

PARENTHESES

> • Use parentheses for material that is not part of the main statement but is important to include.

To add variety to your writing, you may wish to include material in parentheses to your sentences.

Sarah (who would later win the award) bowed at curtain call.

Try It! Read each sentence. If there is material that should be enclosed in parentheses, add the parentheses.

1. The play that the eighth-graders presented was a huge hit.

2. The comedy which was adapted from a short story was so funny.

3. Did you like the first act better than the other two?

4. John the student to my right laughed so hard he almost cried.

5. I saw Mr. Lewis wiping tears from his face.

6. The director who has directed other plays looked very pleased.

7. The actors were so good in their roles.

8. Jacob the lead actor stole the show.

9. He was so funny when he fell over the coffee table.

10. Sarah looked so glamorous in her evening gown.

Write It! Write an explanation of something you know how to do. Be sure to use parentheses correctly in your work.

SYNONYMS

> • A **synonym** is a word that has the same or almost the same meaning as another word.

When you write, you can replace a vague or general word in a sentence with a word that is more precise.

Vague: The story was very *good*.

Precise: The story was very *compelling*.

Try It! Replace the underlined word in each sentence with a synonym that is more precise.

1. The audience for the storyteller was <u>big</u>.   _____

2. The storyteller <u>looked</u> at the audience.   _____

3. Their faces <u>showed</u> their anticipation.   _____

4. Everyone had heard that the storyteller was <u>good</u>.   _____

5. She had several <u>interesting</u> stories in her repertoire.   _____

6. The audience <u>wanted</u> to be entertained.   _____

7. I thought she wore a very <u>nice</u> costume.   _____

8. The man next to me had a bouquet of <u>small</u> rosebuds.   _____

9. He <u>threw</u> it on the stage when she began her story.   _____

10. The storyteller's eyes <u>looked</u> appreciatively at the man.   _____

Write It! Write a description of a person you admire. Be sure to include precise nouns, verbs, and adjectives in your work. Share your description with a classmate. Ask your classmate to identify any words that you might replace with more precise synonyms.

Macmillan/McGraw-Hill

ANTONYMS

> • An **antonym** is a word that has an opposite meaning from another word.

In your writing, you can contrast your ideas by using antonyms.

   The general *lost* the battle but *triumphed* by winning the war.

Try It!   Underline the two antonyms in each sentence.

 1. He was aggressive at first, but became more cautious as time went on.

 2. The enemy's attempt was feeble while his was more energetic.

 3. The clumsy soldier was no match for the graceful horseman.

 4. There was a brief pause in the shooting before the prolonged battle continued.

 5. The small force seemed confident even though the outcome of the battle was still uncertain.

 6. Suddenly a loud cheer was heard in the hushed forest.

 7. Vigorous reinforcements came to replace the tired soldiers.

 8. They would not retire in defeat; instead, victory would be theirs.

 9. The enthusiastic replacements marched past the listless troops.

10. One sad soldier looked at the happy marching men and smiled.

Write It!   Contrast what subject you like best in school this year with the subject you liked best last year. If you use any antonyms in your writing, be sure they are precise.

HOMOGRAPHS

> • **Homographs** are words that are spelled the same but have different meanings and sometimes different pronunciations.

When you read, use the context of the sentence to understand the correct meaning of a homograph.

The *bear* frightened the campers.   (an animal)

She could not *bear* the weather.   (endure)

Try It!   One word in each sentence is a homograph. Underline the homograph.

1. Her rosy complexion was quite fair.

2. Did you wind the grandfather clock?

3. The famous actress took a bow at the end of the performance.

4. I will study plane geometry next year.

5. If I gain another pound, I don't know what I will do.

6. Is the patient's condition stable?

7. Please board the cruiser right now.

8. She bought a yard of the striped fabric.

9. Send your cousin a get-well note.

10. The count married his true love yesterday.

Write It!   Write ten sentences using the homographs from **Try It!** Use another meaning for each homograph in your sentences.

HOMOPHONES

> • **Homophones** are words that sound alike but have different spellings and different meanings.

When you write, be sure to check the spelling of homophones.

There are three sisters.

Their story is a famous one.

They're all in love at the same time.

Try It!   Underline the correct word in parentheses. Use a dictionary if you need one.

1. Sally (red, read) all the books on the book list.

2. The (feat, feet) that the hero performed was pretty amazing.

3. Is (your, you're) book report ready yet?

4. I will give you (sum, some) extra credit for the report.

5. Stop by my office in one (hour, our).

6. You can (here, hear) my report tomorrow in class.

7. The (hole, whole) class will applaud your effort.

8. (Who's, Whose) going to present first?

9. Ted (or, ore) Sam will read first.

10. I will need a (piece, peace) of paper for notes.

Write It!   Use each of the homophones that you did not underline in **Try It!** in a new sentence. Share your sentences with a classmate. Ask your classmate to check your use of homophones.

CONTEXT CLUES

> • The **context** of a sentence can sometimes help you to figure out the meaning of an unfamiliar word. The context includes the other words in the sentence or in nearby sentences.

When you come across an unfamiliar word in your reading, use the other words in the sentence as clues to help you determine the word's meaning.

The *teeming* street scene was filled with busy crowds.

The words *busy* and *crowds* are clues to the meaning of the word *teeming*.

Try It!   Write the meaning of each underlined word. Then use a dictionary to check your work.

1. She whispered <u>furtively</u> even in the middle of the free-

    flowing and open conversation.   _____

2. Her stare was as <u>frigid</u> as ice.   _____

3. His trusty backpack accompanies him on every <u>excursion</u>

    that he takes.   _____

4. Have you ever taken a <u>transatlantic</u> cruise to England?   _____

5. The trip actually cost a <u>pittance</u>, compared to the more

    expensive trips.   _____

6. I was completely <u>disheartened</u> by the sad state of affairs.   _____

7. She tells many <u>anecdotes</u> about all of her travel

    experiences.   _____

8. Sometimes she appears <u>gullible</u> because she believes

    anything you tell her.   _____

9. He had many <u>exploits</u> on his island journey.   _____

10. She was completely <u>dauntless</u> in the face of many of

    the dangers she had on her trip.   _____

Write It!   Find a newspaper article and circle five words that are unfamiliar to you in it. Try to use context clues to tell the meaning of the unfamiliar words. Check a dictionary to see how accurate you were. Then use each word in a sentence.

Macmillan/McGraw-Hill

TROUBLESOME WORDS

> - Some words, such as *good* and *well*, have very specific rules about their usage. Use *good* as an adjective to describe nouns. Use *well* as an adverb to tell about verbs. Use *well* when talking about health.
>
> - Other words, such as *there, their,* and *they're*, have very different meanings. Use *there* to mean a place. Use *their* to show possession. Use *they're* as a contraction to stand for *they are.*
>
> - The words *to, two,* and *too* are sometimes confused. Use *to* to introduce a prepositional phrase or an infinitive. Use *two* as a number. Use *too* as an adverb meaning *also* or a *degree of something.*

When you write, watch out for words that are often confused. Check your dictionary if you need help.

It was a *good* paper.	He wrote very *well*.	The boy felt *well*.
Put it over *there*.	Is that *their* car?	*They're* coming today.
Give it *to* me.	I have *two* cookies.	I will have one, *too*.

Try It!   Underline the correct word in parentheses.

1. The patient said that she was feeling very (good, well).

2. She had been a (good, well) patient for several weeks.

3. Did he do (good, well) on the test?

4. I want to sit (there, their).

5. (They're, Their) a very good example for us.

6. She did (two, to) assignments while I watched television.

7. I think you are spending (too, to) much time with her.

8. Will you give the report (to, too) her tomorrow?

9. Have they given you (their, there) assignment yet?

10. I hope I get a very (good, well) grade on my test.

Write It!   Write a paragraph about something that you do very well. Share your paragraph with a classmate. Ask your classmate to tell you if you have used any of the troublesome words from the lesson incorrectly.

Macmillan/McGraw-Hill

SPECIFIC NOUNS

> • Using **specific nouns** makes your writing more interesting and helps the reader to picture exactly what you want to convey.

When you write, use specific nouns to focus your thoughts and to state your ideas clearly on paper.

Less Specific: My *dog* barked at the *bird*.

More Specific: My *terrier* barked at the *robin*.

Try It!   Change the underlined noun in each sentence to a more specific noun.

1. The <u>flowers</u> in the garden were lovely.   _____

2. I saw a beautiful <u>bird</u> in the birdbath.   _____

3. My <u>pet</u> was intrigued by the grassy meadow.   _____

4. Will you pick a bunch of <u>wildflowers</u>?   _____

5. You can bring them into the <u>house</u>.   _____

6. The <u>man</u> will arrange them into a beautiful display.   _____

7. We can put the flowers in the <u>room</u>.   _____

8. The <u>people</u> will see them when they come in the door.   _____

9. I hope everyone will enjoy the <u>party</u>.   _____

10. We will meet in the other <u>room</u>.   _____

Write It!   Write a paragraph describing a party you have had or attended. Make sure that you use specific nouns in your work.

Macmillan/McGraw-Hill

VIVID VERBS

> • **Vivid verbs** express action precisely and clearly.

When you write, use vivid verbs to help your actions come alive and to help your reader to picture exactly what's happening.

Less Vivid: We *ran* out of the house.

More Vivid: We *dashed* out of the house.

Try It! Change each underlined verb in the sentence to a more vivid verb.

1. We <u>went</u> to the very exciting race.   _____

2. I <u>saw</u> the horses at the starting gate.   _____

3. They <u>left</u> from the gate at the shot of a pistol.   _____

4. The horses <u>ran</u> around the track.   _____

5. The two lead horses <u>were</u> neck and neck.   _____

6. The crowd <u>yelled</u> madly.   _____

7. The galloping horses <u>scared</u> me.   _____

8. My friend <u>looked</u> at me with alarm.   _____

9. When my horse <u>went</u> across the finish line, I could not look.   _____

10. I <u>found</u> my winning ticket in the bottom of my purse.   _____

Write It! Write a story about an adventure you have had or would like to have. Be sure to use vivid verbs in your story.

Macmillan/McGraw-Hill

COLORFUL ADJECTIVES

> • **Adjectives** can add sensory details to your writing. Sensory details refer to one or more of the five senses—sight, hearing, touch, taste, or smell.

Sensory words can make your writing more effective as readers of your writing will re-create in their minds the experience you describe.

The children looked in the window.

The *eager, young* children looked in the *decorated store* window.

Try It!   Add some colorful adjectives to these sentences.

1. The shops were filled with merchandise. _____

2. The floor with toys was enchanting. _____

3. The boys and girls looked at the toys. _____

4. On the fifth floor were the games and videos. _____

5. The shoppers strolled through the store. _____

6. They bought things for their families. _____

7. Did you see that sweater? _____

8. The ties were quite lovely. _____

9. That doll would be perfect for my sister. _____

10. I can't wait to wrap the presents. _____

Write It!   Write a paragraph that describes the best gift you ever received. Be sure to include colorful adjectives in your description.

Macmillan/McGraw-Hill

EXCITING ADVERBS

> • **Exciting adverbs** can add details to your writing that tell *how, when,* and *where.*

Use exciting adverbs whenever possible to make your writing come alive for your reader.

I went to the park.

I *reluctantly went* to the *park yesterday.*

Try It!   Add some exciting adverbs to these sentences.

1. Many children played in the park.   _____

2. The children looked for their toys.   _____

3. Will you see the babysitter?   _____

4. The young girl smiled at the grandmother. _____

5. The little boy looked strong.   _____

6. He pushed the swing for his sister.   _____

7. Tell the noisy children to be quiet.   _____

8. I will be going home.   _____

9. She plays with the other children.   _____

10. I watched her toss the ball.   _____

Write It!   Write a paragraph about your idea of what is fun. Be sure to use exciting adverbs in your paragraph.

Macmillan/McGraw-Hill

PREFIXES

> • A **prefix** is a word part added to the beginning of a base word.
>
> • A prefix changes the meaning of the base word to which it is added.

In your writing, be sure to use the correct prefix to convey your meaning.

Common Prefix	Meaning	Example
de	from, down	depress
inter	between	intercity
pre	before	precede
re	again, back	review
in	without, not	inexpensive
un	not, opposite of	uninformed

Try It!   Underline each word that has a prefix. Write the meaning of the word.

1. I think that book was totally uninteresting. _____

2. I will review it tomorrow. _____

3. It's a science fiction book about interplanetary

   warfare. _____

4. Did you preview it before you bought it? _____

5. I think the purchase of it is indefensible. _____

6. I will reevaluate the book. _____

7. She prepaid the costs of shipping the book. _____

8. The writing is totally incomprehensible. _____

9. I'm sorry I bought *Intergalactic Terror.* _____

10. I will return it immediately. _____

Write It!   Use each of the underlined words from **Try It!** in a sentence of your own. Exchange papers with a classmate. Have your classmate find the words in your sentences and tell you what they mean.

Book of Minilessons, Grades 6–8
Skill   #

SUFFIXES

> • A **suffix** is a word part added to the end of a base word. A suffix changes the meaning of the base word to which it is added. It also changes the part of speech of the base word.

When you write, remember that a suffix changes a word's meaning.

Suffix	Meaning	Example
an (noun)	one that is of	American
er, or, ist (noun)	one who is or does	teacher
ion (noun)	act, state, or result of	protection
able (adjective)	able to	readable
ful (adjective)	full of	sorrowful
ly (adjective)	like	queenly
ly (adverb)	like	busily

Try It!   Underline each word that has a suffix. Then tell the meaning of the word. Use a dictionary if necessary.

1. I went on a European trip.   _____

2. I met a researcher from *National Geographic.*   _____

3. The guide was quite helpful with the tour.   _____

4. He made sure I made my connection.   _____

5. The friendly bus driver gave me a lift.   _____

6. The path to the top of the cliff was manageable.   _____

7. I met another American tourist on the trip.   _____

8. She was a guest speaker at one of the lectures.   _____

9. Her talk was unbelievable.   _____

10. I felt her deep concentration on her subject.   _____

Write It!   Use each of the underlined words from **Try It!** in a sentence. Identify the suffixes in the words in your sentences.

IMAGERY AND PERSONIFICATION

> • **Imagery** is the use of words to create pictures, or images, in the reader's mind.
>
> • **Personification** is a comparison in which human traits are given to objects, ideas, or animals.

You can make your writing more vivid and colorful by using imagery and personification.

Imagery: My trip across the *blazing sands* of Egypt was memorable.

Personification: My trusty sword, *Ahmed*, was always by my side.

Try It!   Underline and label examples of *imagery* and *personification* in the following sentences.

1. On my trip around the world I saw islands that were
   no bigger than tiny dots from the air.   _____

2. The green foliage in the rain forest was dripping with dew.   _____

3. My red jeep, nicknamed Tillie, never failed me.   _____

4. She made it over mountains and through muddy streams.   _____

5. The muddy streams surged sluggishly through the ravines.   _____

6. Tillie got a little water-logged, but she kept on going.   _____

7. The green canopy over my head shut out most of the light.   _____

8. In the rain forest a green calm and quiet prevailed.   _____

9. I left Tillie waiting alone in a clearing and proceeded on foot.   _____

10. Tillie was upset, but I had to enter this place on my own.   _____

Write It!   Write a description of a special place that you know. In your description try to use *imagery* and *personification* to make your writing vivid and colorful.

Macmillan/McGraw-Hill

IDIOMS

> - An **idiom** is an expression whose meaning cannot be grasped from the meaning of the individual words comprising it.
> - Some idioms are considered perfectly appropriate for formal writing, but some are considered more appropriate for informal speech and writing.

The use of idioms can make the dialog in your writing more authentic and interesting.

The bus driver yelled, *"Step on it!"* to the boy.

Try It!   Underline the idioms in the following sentences.

1. I ran across an old friend on the bus today.

2. We had hit it off immediately when we last saw each other.

3. However, now she seemed to be a bit full of herself.

4. We used to hit the books together when we last knew each other.

5. Somewhere along the way she lost her head.

6. She is now nearly always on the go.

7. You really have to shake a leg to keep up with her.

8. She will run you ragged if you don't watch out.

9. I really couldn't get a handle on what she was saying.

10. I was totally at sea by the time we parted.

Write It!   Make a list of idioms that you know or use some from **Try It!** Write a conversation between two people who speak in idioms. Share your work with a friend and have your friend define the idioms.

Macmillan/McGraw-Hill

ALLITERATION AND REPETITION

> • **Alliteration** is the repetition of the same initial sound, usually of a consonant, in a series of words.
>
> • **Repetition** involves repeating words, phrases, or even whole lines.

When you write, you can use *alliteration* and *repetition* to make your writing musical and catchy and to stand out in the reader's mind.

Alliteration: The *nice, neat knick-knack* shelf is for sale.

Repetition: *"Buy it! Buy it!"* said the radio announcer.

Try It!   Underline and label the examples of alliteration and repetition in the following sentences.

1. There are fabulous finds in the antique store.   _____

2. Radiant red radios are on a shelf in the back.   _____

3. In the front on the display case are pretty pink pitchers.   _____

4. A parrot in a cage says, "Howdy, howdy, to you."   _____

5. Miniature motor cars are in a basket up front.   _____

6. Beaded ball gowns hang from the walls.   _____

7. The delightful dolls with satin sashes catch my eye.   _____

8. They sit at a table on which there are tiny teacups.   _____

9. Each corner of the shop beckons, "Come here, come here."   _____

10. I cannot leave without that set of brass buttons.   _____

Write It!   Write an ad for a product. Your product can be real or imaginary. Use *alliteration* and *repetition* in your ad to make it catchy.

SIMILE AND METAPHOR

> - A **simile** uses the word *like* or *as* to compare one thing (person, animal, idea) to another.
> - A **metaphor** is a comparison in which one of two things is said to be the other.

Using similes and metaphors in your writing can make it more vivid and colorful.

Simile: *The river is like a shining ribbon.*

Metaphor: *The river is a winding snake.*

Try It!   Underline and label the *similes* and *metaphors* in the following sentences.

1. My trip to the West was like a bad dream. _____

2. The plane ride to Denver was a nightmare. _____

3. The whir of the propeller was like a pounding drill. _____

4. My head felt as big as a beach ball when we landed. _____

5. The elevation made my heart beat like a hammer. _____

6. The mountain trail was as narrow as a thread. _____

7. The night air was a cold, wet blanket over my head. _____

8. My prepared food tasted like wet cardboard. _____

9. The horse I rode was as stubborn as a mule. _____

10. Civilization was a long-awaited gift. _____

Write It!   Write a description of something that did not turn out as you had expected. Share your work with a classmate. Ask your classmate to identify any similes or metaphors in your work.

Answer Key

Name: _____ Date: _____

SENTENCES

- **A sentence** is a group of words that expresses a complete thought.

When you use complete sentences, your writing will be clear to your reader. Be sure to use correct end punctuation.

Complete: *The Egyptians build pyramids.*
Not Complete: *Built huge pyramids.*

Try It! Write *sentence* next to each group of words that is a sentence.

1. The early civilization of Egypt was noteworthy. _____ sentence

2. The ancient Egyptians developed sophisticated irrigation systems. _____ sentence

3. Able to harness the Nile.

4. Early rulers who were cruel.

5. Slaves were used to build the pyramids. _____ sentence

6. Rulers, along with their belongings, were buried in some pyramids. _____ sentence

7. Egyptians used several methods to preserve the bodies of the dead. _____ sentence

8. Mummies wrapped in cloth.

9. Sealed in airtight containers.

10. Egyptian religion believed in an afterlife. _____ sentence

Write It! Suppose you had to design a pyramid for an Egyptian ruler. Do some research on pyramids and write a short report about them. Be sure that each sentence expresses a complete thought and has the correct end punctuation.

Name: _____ Date: _____

TYPES OF SENTENCES

- A **declarative sentence** makes a statement. It ends with a period.
- An **interrogative sentence** asks a question. It ends with a question mark.
- An **imperative sentence** makes a command or request. It ends with a period.
- An **exclamatory sentence** expresses strong feeling. It ends with an exclamation mark.

When you write, vary the types of sentences you use. This will make your writing more interesting. Remember to punctuate sentences correctly.

Declarative Sentence: *I like pasta very much.*
Interrogative Sentence: *Have you ever had linguine?*
Imperative Sentence: *Prepare the sauce right now.*
Exclamatory Sentence: *Wow, this meal is beyond belief!*

Try It! Add the correct end punctuation to each of the sentences.

1. Our school is having a pasta night to raise money _____ .

2. Are you going to go to the pasta night _____ ?

3. There will be over twenty-five different kinds of pasta _____ .

4. Wow, that's a lot of pasta _____ !

5. Several of my friends are going to go _____ .

6. Don't even think about missing this night _____ . or !

7. Who is cooking all that pasta _____ ?

8. My favorite pasta is linguine with red clam sauce _____ .

9. Good grief, I can't believe you would eat a clam _____ !

10. Go out and buy a ticket right now _____ .

Write It! Write a description of a school event you attended. Be sure to use different types of sentences and punctuate them correctly.

88

SENTENCE FRAGMENTS

Name: _____ Date: _____

> • A **sentence fragment** does not express a complete thought. It lacks either a subject part or a predicate part.

When you write, be sure to use complete sentences. Sentence fragments will confuse your reader.

Fragment (lacks a predicate): *Some friends of mine.*
Fragment (lacks a subject): *Spent their vacation on a safari.*

Try It! Add a subject or a predicate to each of the fragments to make the fragment a complete sentence. **Answers will vary. Possible answers are given.**

1. Going on my first safari. _____ I am
2. Planned my safari for a long time. _____ I have
3. Were anxious to see the game preserves. _____ We
4. The parents and their two teen-age children. _____ were eager to go
5. The guide on the safari. _____ was very brave
6. Rode in jeeps and trucks. _____ The family
7. The herd of giraffes. _____ They photographed
8. Several elephants and their babies. _____ came up to the jeep
9. A severe dust storm. _____ slowed them down
10. Had to leave for the trip home. _____ They

Write It! Imagine that you could go on a trip of your choice. What would it be? Where would you go? Write a description of your ideal trip. Be sure to use complete sentences and to punctuate them correctly.

RUN-ON SENTENCES

Name: _____ Date: _____

> • A **run-on sentence** joins two or more sentences that should be written separately.

Be sure to avoid run-on sentences when you write. Rewrite each part of the run-on as a complete sentence so that your readers will not be confused.

Run-on: *Sojourner Truth was an enslaved woman she wrote about her experiences.*
Correct: *Sojourner Truth was an enslaved woman. She wrote about her experiences.*

Try It! Write *run-on* next to each sentence that is a run-on sentence.

1. Sojourner Truth was born in New York in 1795.
2. When she was born, her name was Isabella van Hardenbergh.
3. She was named for her enslaver's family she objected to that. _____ run-on
4. She changed her name when slavery was abolished in New York State because she wished to leave her past behind.
5. Sojourner Truth believed in women's rights she opposed slavery. _____ run-on
6. Women who were enslaved did hard work it was as hard as work that the men did. _____ run-on
7. Sojourner Truth traveled throughout the North speaking for women's rights and equality.
8. She chose the name Truth she thought her mission was to tell the truth about the hardships and evil of slavery. _____ run-on
9. Sojourner Truth was a brave and honorable woman.
10. She did much to expose the evils of slavery and to promote equality for women.

Write It! Find out more information about Sojourner Truth and write a short report about her. Be sure to check that your sentences are complete and that you have no run-on sentences in your report.

COMPLETE SUBJECTS AND PREDICATES

> - The **complete subject** includes all the words that tell whom or what the sentence is about.
> - The **complete predicate** includes all the words that tell what the subject does or is.

When you write it is important that your sentences have both a complete subject and a complete predicate. Otherwise, you have written a sentence fragment, which may confuse your readers.

Complete Subject   **Complete Predicate**

The tiny spider   *was grey and delicate looking.*

Try It! Draw one line under the complete subject and two lines under the complete predicate.

1. *Charlotte's Web* by E. B. White is a children's classic.

2. E. B. White was a published poet and essayist.

3. This noted writer wrote for the *New Yorker* magazine.

4. He entertained adult audiences for years.

5. White surprised everyone with his book about a pig named Wilbur.

6. Wilbur and Charlotte, the spider, become the best of friends.

7. The other characters in the barnyard were friends with them, too.

8. Fern is a spunky and loyal little girl in the story.

9. Fern takes care of Wilbur until he is a grown pig.

10. Charlotte saves Wilbur's life.

Write It! What is your favorite book? Write a book report about it. Make sure that all of your sentences have both a complete subject and a complete predicate.

SIMPLE SUBJECTS AND PREDICATES

> - The **simple subject** is the main word or words in the complete subject.
> - The **simple predicate** is the main word or words in the complete predicate.

When you write, be sure that your sentences are complete. If your sentences are not complete, your message will not be clear to your reader.

Simple Subject   **Simple Predicate**

*Today's modern **elevator***   ***was invented** by Elisha Otis.*

Try It! Draw one line under the simple subject. Draw two lines under the simple predicate.

1. Elisha Otis built a factory in New York.

2. The factory needed a lifting device for its employees.

3. This inventor drew a plan for such a device.

4. Otis named his first machine the "safety hoister."

5. The audience screamed in terror at the first demonstration of the elevator.

6. The first passenger elevator was built for a hotel.

7. Today elevators reach the topmost floors in buildings.

8. Some buildings have more than 100 floors.

9. Elevator inspectors inspect elevators every year.

10. Safety is a very important issue in elevators.

Write It! Who is your favorite inventor? Write a short biographical sketch of the inventor. Make sure that your sentences are complete. You may want to have a friend check your work.

Name: _____ Date: _____

COMPOUND SUBJECTS AND PREDICATES

- A **compound subject** is two or more simple subjects with the same predicate.
- A **compound predicate** is two or more simple predicates with the same subject.
- A **coordinating conjunction** such as *and*, *or*, or *but* connects the parts of a compound subject or predicate.

Using compound subjects and predicates can add variety to your writing.

Compound Subject: *Dorrie and Janet* went to the mall.

Compound Predicate: They *shopped and ate dinner at a nice restaurant.*

Try It! Label each sentence with *CS* for compound subject or with *CP* for compound predicate. If the sentence does not have either, label it *N*.

1. The mall has many beautiful stores. **N**

2. The shoppers walk briskly and carry many packages. **CP**

3. Parents and their children stroll along slowly. **CS**

4. Did you see that huge bookstore? **N**

5. Janet will buy a gift and send it to her niece. **CP**

6. Dorrie and her friend come to the mall at least once a month. **CS**

7. They browse in the music store and buy several CDs. **CP**

8. A huge tour bus has brought many customers to the mall. **N**

9. Janet, Dorrie, and the clerk are finding the right sizes. **CS**

10. Customers and tourists talk to each other at the mall. **CS**

Write It! Have you ever been to a mall? What did you do there? Write a paragraph about a trip to the mall. Try to include sentences that have compound subjects and compound predicates in your paragraph.

Name: _____ Date: _____

COMPOUND SENTENCES

- A **simple sentence** has one complete subject and one complete predicate.
- A **compound sentence** has two or more simple sentences joined by *and*, *but*, or *or*, preceded by a comma.

When you write, be sure that your sentences are complete and that you vary your sentences. Some sentences can be compound sentences.

Simple sentence: *The members of the school committee met today.*

Compound sentence: *The school committee met, and they voted quickly.*

Try It! Label each sentence *simple* or *compound*.

1. The school committee was formed to deal with problems at Lake Middle School. **simple**

2. Sarah Hathaway is president, and she works hard at her job. **compound**

3. The committee has four representatives from our grade. **simple**

4. Don Hicks is the best representative, but he misses some meetings. **compound**

5. He takes very good notes, or he uses his tape recorder at meetings. **compound**

6. I ran for the committee, but I was defeated by Jane Harris. **compound**

7. Next year I will run again, and you can be my campaign manager. **compound**

8. The committee proposes many laws for us to consider. **simple**

9. It's just like government in action. **simple**

10. I will need a platform for next year, and I will start my campaign right now. **compound**

Write It! Have you ever run for a school office or helped someone else? What would your platform be? Think of some issues and write a paragraph that persuades people to vote for you. Be sure to use some compound sentences in your paragraph.

Name: _____ Date: _____

COMPLEX SENTENCES

- A **subordinate clause** is a group of words that has a subject and a predicate, but cannot stand alone as a complete sentence.
- A **complex sentence** contains an independent clause, which is a group of words that can stand alone as a complete sentence, and one or more subordinate clauses.

When you write, remember to put a comma after the subordinate clause if it comes at the beginning of the sentence.

Before the colonists sailed, they made sure they had adequate supplies.
The colonists were fearful *because they did not know what to expect.*

Try It! Draw one line under the subordinate clause.

1. Although they had good supplies, the colonists almost did not survive.

2. They faced many hardships because the voyage to America was long.

3. When they arrived at Jamestown, they found the winter harsh.

4. Native Americans helped them when they first arrived.

5. Though the Native Americans helped them, the colonists had to learn to survive on their own.

6. Though John Smith was a fine leader, he could not do it all.

7. The government of Jamestown had to be secure before other colonists would come from England.

8. If disease or sickness came to Jamestown, very few would be able to survive without doctors.

9. Professional people would not make the trip to America unless they could be sure of their safety.

10. When the colony survived its first year, everyone was ecstatic.

Write It! Do some research about the Colonial period in American history. Write a short report about what you find. Share your report with a classmate. Can your classmate identify the complex sentences?

Name: _____ Date: _____

ADJECTIVE AND ADVERB CLAUSES

- An **adjective clause** is a subordinate clause that modifies, or describes, a noun or pronoun in the independent clause of a complex sentence.
- An **adverb clause** modifies the verb in the independent clause of a complex sentence.

When you write, be sure to use a comma after an adverb clause that comes at the beginning of the sentence.

Adjective Clause: Sheri has a necklace *that is handmade.*

Adverb Clause: She has owned it *since she was very young.*

Try It! Draw one line under the adjective or adverb clause. Draw two lines under the word it modifies.

1. Sheri loves her locket because her grandmother gave it to her.

2. When Sheri was a baby, her grandmother bought it for her.

3. It was her grandmother who found the locket in the antique store.

4. It had a small heart that reminded her of her new granddaughter.

5. Her grandmother bought it because Sheri had just been born.

6. She kept it until she was sure Sheri wouldn't swallow it!

7. Grandmother was a woman who was very concerned with safety.

8. Although Sheri wanted the locket now, her grandmother waited.

9. Sheri was nine years old before her grandmother gave her the locket.

10. Because she had to wait so long, Sheri treasured her locket more.

Write It! Suppose you received a lovely gift from someone. Write a thank you letter for the gift. Then share your letter with a friend. Can your friend point out any adjective or adverb clauses?

91

Name: _____   Date: _____

KINDS OF NOUNS

- A **noun** is a word that names a person, place, thing, or idea.
- A **common noun** names a nonspecific person, place, thing, or idea.
- A **proper noun** names a specific person, place, thing, or idea. A proper noun begins with a capital letter.

When you write, be sure to capitalize proper nouns.

Common Noun	Proper Noun	Common Noun	Proper Noun
cousin	Linda	mountain	Mount Everest
month	July	city	Los Angeles
planet	Saturn	time	Ice Age

Try It! Draw one line under each common noun and two lines under each proper noun.

1. Linda, my cousin, has visited almost every state.

2. Her favorite state is North Carolina.

3. It is one of the best places on Earth as far as she is concerned.

4. The Smoky Mountains are magnificent.

5. The trees, gently sloping foothills, and streams are beautiful.

6. A ranger took Linda and her friends on a tour of the hiking paths.

7. They found interesting samples of rocks while she walked the hills.

8. Many small towns in North Carolina have interesting crafts.

9. Beautiful carvings are made from wood by the people of Boone.

10. Asheville is the home of the Biltmore Mansion, a huge house built by the Vanderbilts.

Write It! What is your favorite state in the United States? Is it the one in which you live? Write a description of your favorite state. Be sure to include some proper nouns.

Name: _____   Date: _____

SINGULAR AND PLURAL NOUNS

- A **singular noun** is a noun that names one person, place, thing, or idea.
- A **plural noun** is a noun that names more than one person, place, thing, or idea. Add s or es to most singular nouns to make them plural.

When you write make sure that you use plural nouns correctly.

Singular:	girl	house	bush	civilization
Plural:	girls	houses	bushes	civilizations

Try It! Draw one line under each singular noun. Draw two lines under each plural noun.

1. My favorite class in school is English.

2. Of all the classes I take, English is the most interesting.

3. We read a new book every week in my class.

4. Mysteries are my favorite books because I love to figure out who did it.

5. By the end of the semester, the class had read almost 50 books.

6. We have to report on the books we read each month.

7. One month, I read almost 800 pages.

8. In my report, I compared all the books I read.

9. My teacher thought my report was excellent.

10. The next month, my best friend and I wrote our reports together.

Write It! Suppose that you and a friend are planning to do a school project together. Write a plan for your project. List the steps that you will follow. Then see if you can identify the singular and plural nouns in your plan.

PROPER NOUNS—PEOPLE

- A **proper noun** names a specific person, place, thing, or idea.
- A proper noun begins with a capital letter.

When you write, be sure to begin each proper noun with a capital letter.

Senator Jill Evans   Cousin Marc   M. K. Jones   Liz Stone, M.S.

Try It! Write each proper noun, using the correct capitalization.

1. mary kelly _____ **Mary Kelly**
2. c. k. harrison _____ **C. K. Harrisson**
3. general lawrence smith _____ **General Lawrence Smith**
4. aunt sylvia _____ **Aunt Sylvia**
5. leona pak, ph. d. _____ **Leona Pak, Ph.D.**
6. riverhead fire department 6 _____ **Riverhead Fire Department 6**
7. uncle milton _____ **Uncle Milton**
8. george c. little _____ **George C. Little**
9. chief joseph _____ **Chief Joseph**
10. atlantic avenue _____ **Atlantic Avenue**

Write It! Think of a relative that you like very much. Write a paragraph about a time you spent together. Be sure to capitalize any proper nouns you use in your paragraph.

PROPER NOUNS—PLACES

- A **proper noun** names a specific person, place, thing, or idea.
- Capitalize all proper nouns.

When you write, you can use proper nouns when you wish to be more specific about places.

Australia   Sacramento   Pacific Ocean   Saturn

Try It! Write each proper noun, using the correct capitalization. Then, on a separate sheet of paper, write a sentence using the proper noun.

1. phoenix, arizona _____ **Phoenix, Arizona**
2. france _____ **France**
3. north america _____ **North America**
4. baltic sea _____ **Baltic Sea**
5. empire state building _____ **Empire State Building**
6. bay bridge _____ **Bay Bridge**
7. cascades national park _____ **Cascades National Park**
8. washington monument _____ **Washington Monument**
9. milky way _____ **Milky Way**
10. 1222 tulip lane _____ **1222 Tulip Lane**

Write It! Have you ever visited a national park or a national monument? Write a travel brochure for a place you have visited or would like to visit. Be sure to capitalize all proper nouns.

Name: _____   Date: _____

POSSESSIVE NOUNS

- A **possessive noun** is a noun that names who or what has something.
- Use an **apostrophe** and *s* ('s) to form the possessive of most singular nouns and of plural nouns that do not end in s.
- Use only an **apostrophe** (') to form the possessive of plural nouns that end in s.

John's book   Marie's ball   the boys' toys   the children's hats

When you write, be sure to use apostrophes correctly with possessive nouns.

Try It!   Rewrite each phrase, using a possessive noun. Tell whether the possessive noun is singular or plural.

1. the collar of the dog   the dog's collar; singular
2. the votes of the judges   the judges' votes; plural
3. the poodle of the owner   the owner's poodle; singular
4. the reactions of the audience   the audience's reaction; singular
5. the barks of the contestants   the contestants' barks; plural
6. the dog show of the state   the state's dog show; singular
7. the collie of Susan Kelly   Susan Kelly's collie; singular
8. the awards of the show   the show's awards; singular
9. the ribbons of the winners   the winners' ribbons; plural
10. the first prize of the terrier the terrier's first prize; singular

Write It!   Suppose you entered a favorite pet in a pet show. What would the experience be like? Write a paragraph that tells about this event. Be sure to punctuate correctly any possessive nouns that you use.

Book of Minilessons, Grades 6–8
Skill #

15

Name: _____   Date: _____

COLLECTIVE NOUNS

- A **collective noun** names a group of people or things.
- When the collective noun refers to a group as a whole, use a singular verb.
- When the collective noun refers to the individual members of the group, use the plural form of the verb.

When you use collective nouns in your writing, be sure to use the correct form of the verb.

The *family talk* over their problems together. **plural**
The *family spends* a lot of time outdoors. **singular**

Try It!   Draw one line under each collective noun. Tell whether it is singular or plural.

1. The staff believes in the new representative.   singular
2. The team talk among themselves about the news.   plural
3. The army marches at a steady pace.   singular
4. The public is not in support of the invasion.   singular
5. The group votes for the law in the next session.   singular
6. The audience react in many different ways.   plural
7. A committee sits quietly in the corner of the meeting room.   singular
8. The jury is not in agreement about the verdict.   singular
9. A crowd watches as the people file by.   singular
10. The congress sits in session all next week.   singular

Write It!   Think of something that you like to do with a group. Write a paragraph about it. If you use any collective nouns in your paragraph, be sure that you use the correct form of the verb.

Book of Minilessons, Grades 6–8
Skill

16

94

ACTION VERBS

- An **action verb** is a word that expresses action.

In your writing, be sure to use vivid action verbs so that your reader will be interested in your writing. Remember that an action verb can express mental action as well as physical action.

Whales *swim* far out in the ocean.
They *leap* gracefully into the air despite their size.
The scientist *ponders* their great size.

Try It! Underline the action verbs. Tell whether the action verb expresses mental or physical action.

1. The field and track events start at 9:00 A.M. on Tuesday. _physical_
2. Everyone crowds onto the field. _physical_
3. The sprinters crouch at the starting line. _physical_
4. Coach Jenkins smiles at the crowds. _physical_
5. Assistants place the hurdles on the track. _physical_
6. The javelin throwers stand at attention. _physical_
7. The temperature soars higher and higher. _physical_
8. The relay racers speed around the track. _physical_
9. Everyone enjoyed the day. _mental_
10. I remembered the day for a long time. _mental_

Write It! Suppose you were participating in a track and field event. Which one would it be? Write a paragraph telling about the event you chose. Be sure to use vivid verbs in your paragraph.

APPOSITIVES

- An **appositive** is a word or group of words that follows a noun and identifies or explains it.
- Use commas to set off most appositives.

Be sure to set off most appositives that you use in your writing with commas.

Try-outs for *Alone in the City*, a delightful new comedy, will be held Tuesday.

Try It! Underline the appositive in each sentence. Then add commas where they are needed.

1. Mr. Jones, our drama teacher, will hold try-outs tomorrow.
2. The role of Mona, the biggest part in the play, is the one I want.
3. Most of my friends, wonderful actresses in every way, are going to try out, too.
4. The play, a comedy in three acts, is just hysterical.
5. The playwright, a new writer, has written a great play.
6. Mona, a girl alone in the city, meets a strange old lady.
7. The strange old lady, a real character, won't leave Mona alone.
8. Mona, a cautious girl, doesn't know what to do.
9. She enlists the help of her friend, a private detective.
10. The play, a true theatrical treat, will surprise and delight you.

Write It! Have you seen a good movie or a great play lately or read a good book? Write a review of a movie, play, or book. If you use appositives, be sure to use the correct punctuation.

LINKING VERBS

- A **linking verb** connects the subject of a sentence with a predicate noun or a predicate adjective. A linking verb does not show action.
- A **predicate noun** renames or identifies the subject.
- A **predicate adjective** describes the subject.

In your writing, you can use various kinds of verbs, linking and action, to add variety to your written work.

The winner was *Teddy*.   **predicate noun**

The winner was *overjoyed*.   **predicate adjective**

Try It!   Draw one line under a linking verb. Draw two lines under an action verb.

1. The school essay contest began today.

2. Last year's winner was Leslie Cassidy.

3. She is an excellent writer and thinker.

4. Her essay was extremely well written.

5. Leslie helps others in her class.

6. The second-place winner was Jonathan Park.

7. I want the prize this year.

8. "Why Students Should Be Heard" is the title of my essay.

9. My essay is more humorous than others.

10. My brother laughed at some of the points in my essay.

Write It!   Is there an issue you feel strongly about? Write an essay that tries to convince your audience to feel as you do. Share your essay with a friend. Can your friend identify any linking verbs?

DIRECT OBJECTS, TRANSITIVE AND INTRANSITIVE VERBS

- A **direct object** is a noun or pronoun in the predicate that receives the action of the verb.
- A **transitive verb** has a direct object.
- An **intransitive verb** does not have a direct object.

Keep in mind when you write that a direct object can be two or more nouns or pronouns.

The Spanish built *missions* in the United States.

They brought *religion* and *education* to the people of the area.

The teacher taught *him* and *me* about the missionaries.

Try It!   Draw one line under the verb. Draw two lines under any direct objects. Label the verbs *transitive* or *intransitive*.

1. Spanish missionaries taught their language to the Native Americans.   transitive

2. They gave food and shelter to them as well.   transitive

3. In return Native Americans received religious instruction.   transitive

4. Mission life was very complex.   intransitive

5. Everyone said prayers in the morning and in the evening.   transitive

6. Missionaries kept gardens inside the mission walls.   transitive

7. Native Americans grew food for themselves and for the priests.   transitive

8. Education was important to everyone.   intransitive

9. Many missions still stand today in California and Texas.   intransitive

10. The missions represent a part of our nation's history.   transitive

Write It!   Conduct some research on Spanish missions of California and Texas. Write a short report about one mission. Make sure to use vivid and varied verbs in your report.

ACTIVE AND PASSIVE VOICES

- A verb is in the **active voice** when the subject of the sentence performs the action. Verbs in the active voice may or may not have a direct object.
- A verb is in the **passive voice** when the subject of the sentence receives the action. Verbs in the passive voice do not have a direct object.

Using verbs in the active voice can make your writing stronger.

The hikers greeted the ranger.   **active voice**

The hikers were approached by the ranger.   **passive voice**

Try It!   Tell whether the verb in each sentence is in the active or passive voice.

1. The hikers were frightened by the rough trails. _____ passive

2. However, they struggled onward to the top of the foothill. _____ active

3. At the top they were met by the other group of hikers. _____ passive

4. The hikers exchanged stories with each other. _____ active

5. The hike had been planned by very experienced hikers. _____ passive

6. Great fun was had by all despite the difficulties. _____ passive

7. The campfire cast a rosy glow on the campers' faces. _____ active

8. The stories were told in a very funny way. _____ passive

9. Bret was reduced to hysterical laughter at one point. _____ passive

10. The campers gave each other their addresses. _____ active

Write It!   Describe the best camping, hiking, or field trip that you have had. When you have finished your description, look for any sentences in the passive voice. Change the verbs in those sentences to the active voice.

INDIRECT OBJECTS

- An **indirect object** is a noun or a pronoun in the predicate that answers the question *to whom? for whom? to what?* or *for what?* after an action verb.

When you write, remember that sentences with an indirect object must also have a direct object. Remember that both direct objects and indirect objects can be two or more words.

    indirect object   direct object

Sally gave *Jason* the history *book.*

  indirect   direct
  object   object

Jason showed *me* the *book* and the *report.*

Try It!   Draw one line under the indirect object. Draw two lines under the direct object.

1. Sally showed me a report on Greece.

2. She told the class some interesting facts about Greek warfare.

3. The Greek army offered its soldiers no choice.

4. The battles brought both sides much sorrow.

5. The wars caused Greece hardship and suffering.

6. Great heroes often gave each other grave wounds.

7. Achilles won his country freedom from oppression.

8. The Greek gods gave Achilles much good fortune.

9. Achilles brought his country fame and fortune.

10. Vulcan gave Achilles a magical set of armor.

Write It!   What is your favorite myth? Write a paragraph of explanation about your favorite myth. Then, share your paragraph with a classmate. Can your friend identify the direct and indirect objects in your writing?

98

Name: _____   Date: _____

SUBJECT-VERB AGREEMENT

- A verb must agree in number with its subject. Use a singular verb with a singular subject and a plural verb with a plural subject.
- A verb must agree with its subject even if the verb comes before the subject or the verb is separated from the subject.

The **divers use** a great deal of equipment.
The team **leader uses** several pieces of heavy apparatus.
Did they use the aqualung?

When you write, be sure that your subjects and verbs agree so that your reader will not be confused.

Try It!   Underline the correct form of the verb in parentheses.

1. Jacques Cousteau (study, studies) life under the sea.

2. His assistants (help, helps) him on his voyages.

3. Divers (use, uses) aqualungs when they dive beneath the sea.

4. The experts (check, checks) the aqualungs very carefully.

5. Cousteau (give, gives) many lectures to students and to the public.

6. Members of the audience (ask, asks) him many questions.

7. (Is, Are) he happy to share his information?

8. The underwater explorers (find, finds) interesting facts about the sea.

9. They (spend, spends) hours under water.

10. Could you (live, lives) under water for a great length of time?

Write It!   Imagine that you were going to interview Jacques Cousteau. What questions would you ask him? Write five questions that you would like answered. Make sure that your subjects agree with your verbs.

Name: _____   Date: _____

PRESENT, PAST, AND FUTURE TENSES

- The **present tense** of a verb tells that something is happening now or happens repeatedly.
- The **past tense** of a verb shows an action that has already happened.
- The **future tense** of a verb shows an action that will take place in the future.

I *see* the tall ships today.   **present tense**
I *saw* the tall ships yesterday.   **past tense**
I *will see* the tall ships again tomorrow.   **future tense**

When you write, be sure to use the correct verb tenses so that your reader will understand when the action is taking place.

Try It!   Draw one line under the verb. Tell the tense of the verb.

1. Sarah saw the ships in the harbor yesterday.   _past_

2. The ships had signal flags on them.   _past_

3. The flags will fly in the wind at sea.   _future_

4. The green and white flag flew above the mast.   _past_

5. The wind blows very hard in the North Atlantic.   _present_

6. Sarah draws her own flag designs.   _present_

7. Her brother gave her a book about flags when she was young.   _past_

8. Sarah will design a special flag for her dad's boat.   _future_

9. She also knows quite a bit about flag codes.   _present_

10. She explained flag codes to our class last year.   _past_

Write It!   Imagine that you had to design a secret code for some sailing ships. How would you go about it? Write an explanation. Make sure that you use correct verb tenses in your explanation.

IRREGULAR VERBS

> • The past and past participle forms of **irregular verbs** do not end in *ed*.

Most past-tense verbs end in *ed*, but irregular verbs do not. When you write, make sure to use the correct form of an irregular verb. Refer to your textbook for charts that show irregular verb forms.

Present	Past	Past Participle
be (is, are)	was, were	(have, has, had) been
come	came	(have, has, had) come
bring	brought	(have, has, had) brought
sit	sat	(have, has, had) sat

Try It! Underline the correct past or past participle form of the verb in parentheses.

1. The literary contest (was, has been) yesterday.

2. John (bring, brought) his poetry to the reading.

3. He (choose, chose) the environment as his subject.

4. He (saw, seen) a film about the rain forest that inspired him.

5. His teacher (had spoke, had spoken) highly of the film.

6. John (know, knew) quite a bit about the rain forest anyway.

7. He (had wrote, had written) a first draft for his poem.

8. The ending (gave, given) him quite a bit of trouble.

9. He (had went, had gone) to the contest expecting very little.

10. He (was, has been) surprised by the award.

Write It! Imagine that you have won an award for something that you wrote or accomplished. Write an acceptance speech. Be sure to use the correct forms of irregular verbs in your speech.

VERB PHRASES

> • A **verb phrase** consists of a main verb and all of its helping verbs.
> • A **helping verb** helps the main verb to show an action or make a statement.

When you write, keep in mind that your verbs, and verb phrases, must agree with their subjects.

    main **helping**

Dr. Jones *was working* in the South Pacific.
His helper *can dive* to great ocean depths.

Try It! Draw one line under the main verb. Draw two lines under the helping verb.

1. His assistant has studied the South Pacific for years.

2. She has wondered about the tides her whole life.

3. She has photographed exotic creatures for decades.

4. Dr. Jones has invented a game about sea life.

5. Several of my friends were playing it recently.

6. Sam and June have mastered the game already.

7. Dr. Jones and his assistant were playing it with us.

8. They can answer all of the questions about sea life.

9. They will explain everything about the area.

10. The South Pacific has intrigued them, and they have created a game because of their interest in it.

Write It! Imagine that you are editor of your school newspaper and that you have to write an article about a recent event at school. Write one or two paragraphs about the event. Identify verb phrases and helping verbs in your work.

Name: _____ Date: _____

PRESENT AND PAST PROGRESSIVE VERB FORMS

- The **present progressive** form of a verb expresses action that is continuing now.
- The **past progressive** form of a verb expresses action that continued for some time in the past.
- Progressive forms are made up of a form of *be* and the present participle.

Present Progressive Form
I am singing.
She is singing.
They are singing.

Past Progressive Form
I was singing.
She was singing.
They were singing.

Be sure that you use the correct verb forms in you writing so that your reader will not be confused.

Try It! Underline the verb phrase in each sentence. Tell whether it is *present progressive* or *past progressive*.

1. The movie theater is showing the latest adventure film. — present
2. The theater is presenting the first 100 customers with free popcorn. — present
3. Several groups were viewing the film yesterday. — past
4. The owner was expecting a much smaller turn-out. — past
5. The young stars are attracting a lot of attention. — present
6. The film critic was explaining the plot to several people. — past
7. I am planning another visit to this theater. — present
8. I am looking forward to my next viewing. — present
9. Many people are leaving the theater now. — present
10. I am going inside the theater again right now. — present

Write It! Write a paragraph that summarizes a movie you have recently seen. Give your opinion of the movie. Use and identify present and past progressive forms in your summary.

Book of Minilessons, Grades 6–8
Skill #

27

Name: _____ Date: _____

PERFECT TENSES

- The **present perfect tense** of a verb expresses an action that happened at an indefinite time in the past or that started in the past and is still happening in the present.
- The **past perfect tense** expresses an action that was completed before another past action.
- The **future perfect tense** expresses an action that will be completed in the future before some other future event.

John *has collected* films about figure skating for years. **present perfect**
He *had collected* them before he learned to skate. **past perfect**
He *will have collected* 50 before next autumn. **future perfect**

When you write, make sure that you use the correct verb tenses so that your reader will understand the time order of your writing.

Try It! Underline the verb in each sentence and tell its tense.

1. Larry has followed the career of that famous skater. — present perfect
2. Skating has fascinated him since his childhood. — present perfect
3. He had learned about skating by the age of five. — past perfect
4. Larry has revealed a real talent for figure skating himself. — present perfect
5. By graduation, Larry will have performed in several competitions. — future perfect
6. He has collected hundreds of videos of all the greats. — present perfect
7. Larry has studied their special moves. — present perfect
8. He had watched over 200 hours of tapes before his first competition. — past perfect
9. No wonder he will have completed so many hours on the ice. — future perfect
10. Larry has recognized his own talent at last. — present perfect

Write It! Write a biography of someone you admire. Perhaps it is someone in the entertainment or sports field. Identify the perfect tense verbs in your work.

Book of Minilessons, Grades 6–8
Skill #

28

PRONOUNS

- A **pronoun** takes the place of one or more nouns and the words that go with them.
- Use a **subject pronoun** as the subject of a sentence. Use an **object pronoun** as the object of a verb or a preposition.

Use personal pronouns in your writing to take the place of nouns so that you do not repeat nouns over and over again.

The *boys* stood on the pier.	*They* were fishing.
That *girl* is very funny.	*She* tells lots of jokes and stories.
Give the book to *Jim*.	I will give the book to *him*.

Try It! Underline the pronoun in each sentence.

1. Abraham Lincoln has always fascinated me.
2. He was President during a difficult time.
3. Southerners did not agree with him very much.
4. They thought he did not understand the situation in the South.
5. Nonetheless, he fought for what he believed in.
6. Susan wrote a report on him for history class.
7. She pointed out many things that I did not know about him.
8. She mentioned that he suffered from great sadness.
9. He must have felt very alone when people disagreed with him.
10. I believe he was very brave.

Write It! Write a report about the Civil War in this country. In your report consider some of the great generals on both sides. Share your report with a friend. Ask your friend to identify the personal pronouns.

SUBJECT AND OBJECT PRONOUNS

- Use a **subject pronoun** as the subject of a sentence.
- Use an **object pronoun** as the object of a verb or preposition.

When you write, be sure to use subject and object pronouns correctly.

Subject Pronouns		Object Pronouns	
Singular	**Plural**	**Singular**	**Plural**
I	we	me	us
you	you	you	you
he, she, it	they	him, her, it	them

Try It! Draw one line under each pronoun. Tell whether the pronoun is a *subject pronoun* or an *object pronoun*.

1. I will attend the concert with Josie and Frank. _____ subject
2. They will get the tickets at the box office. _____ subject
3. Frank will pay me for the tickets. _____ object
4. I hope that Josie will go to dinner with us. _____ subject, object
5. Please tell them the name of the restaurant. _____ object
6. They will hold the reservation for us. _____ subject, object
7. Josie told him where to meet us. _____ object, object
8. You can come with her to the concert. _____ subject, object
9. The concert promises to be fun for us. _____ object
10. I can't wait to see it. _____ subject, object

Write It! Write a review of a concert that you attended. Who played at the concert? How did you like it? Give your opinion of the concert. Identify the subject and object pronouns in your review.

101

PRONOUN-ANTECEDENT AGREEMENT

Name: _____ Date: _____

- An **antecedent** is a word or group of words to which a pronoun refers.
- A pronoun must always agree with its antecedent in number and in gender.

When you write, make sure that your pronouns agree with their antecedents so that your readers will not be confused.

Antecedents   **Pronouns**

The battle was lost.   *It* was over in minutes.

General Custer was defeated.   *He* lost the battle.

Try It! Draw one line under the pronoun. Draw two lines under its antecedent.

1. Sue loves American history. She is fascinated by the battles.

2. Wars have played a large part in U.S. history. They have been turning points for events that occurred later.

3. The Battle of The Alamo was significant. It paved the way for Texan independence from Mexico.

4. Mr. Jones is the history teacher. He makes history come alive.

5. Have the students heard of the Battle of San Jacinto? Mr. Jones says it was an important battle.

6. Sam Houston fought in the Battle of San Jacinto. He became a hero.

7. Santa Anna was the leader of the Mexican army. Santa Anna led it to many victories.

8. History is a fascinating subject. It is a subject full of interesting facts and details.

9. Sue may be a history teacher. She would make a very good teacher.

10. Sue would make the subject interesting for the students. Sue would make history come alive for them.

Write It! What is your favorite school subject? Write a paragraph about your favorite subject. Identify the pronouns and antecedents.

Book of Minilessons, Grades 6–8
Skill

31

INDEFINITE PRONOUNS

Name: _____ Date: _____

- An **indefinite pronoun** does not refer to a particular person, place, or thing.
- Any possessive pronoun *(hers, his, ours, mine)* used with an indefinite pronoun must agree with it in number and gender.

When you write make sure that you use indefinite pronouns correctly. Your textbook will have a complete list of indefinite pronouns.

Indefinite Pronouns

Singular: *another, each, everything, nobody, someone, somebody*

Plural: *both, few, many, others, several*

Singular or Plural: *all, any, most, none, some*

Try It! Draw one line under each indefinite pronoun. Tell whether it is singular or plural.

1. Most of the bulbs blew out.   plural

2. One of ours did, too.   singular

3. All of us sat in the dark and wondered what to do.   plural

4. Some of the people looked very nervous.   plural

5. Others looked calm, but I knew they were worried.   plural

6. Most of the guests had left a long time ago.   plural

7. Each person was lost in his or her thoughts.   singular

8. Several of the people went to look for more light bulbs.   plural

9. None of them looked too optimistic.   plural

10. Nobody in the large, dark room moved until the light went on.   singular

Write It! Has anything unexpected ever happened to you? Write a story about that time. Share your story with a friend. Have your friend identify the indefinite pronouns.

Book of Minilessons, Grades 6–8
Skill

32

102

POSSESSIVE PRONOUNS

- A **possessive pronoun** shows who or what owns something.
- Possessive pronouns can come before a noun or stand alone.
- Possessive pronouns never have apostrophes.

Remember that possessive pronouns do not have apostrophes. When you write, make sure to use possessive pronouns correctly.

Janet's speech was excellent. *Her speech* was the best. *Hers* was the best.

Try It! Draw a line under the possessive pronoun in each sentence. Tell whether it comes before the noun or stands alone.

1. My report is about Mother Jones. _____ before
2. Her goal was to get better working conditions for laborers. _____ before
3. Hers was a life of hard work and danger. _____ alone
4. A victim of oppression in Ireland, she fought its evil effects. _____ before
5. Eugene V. Debs was a friend of hers. _____ alone
6. His work in organizing labor unions helped Mother Jones. _____ before
7. The coal miners of West Virginia welcomed her help. _____ before
8. Our country benefited from the work of Mother Jones. _____ before
9. Working conditions were improved for her supporters. _____ before
10. Perhaps the lives of your ancestors were improved, too. _____ before

Write It! Do you have a hero or heroine? Is it someone who helped the poor or disadvantaged? Write a report about your hero or heroine. Identify any possessive pronouns in your report.

CONTRACTIONS

- A **contraction** is a word made by combining two words into one by leaving out one or more letters.

You can make your writing more informal when you use contractions. Be sure to punctuate contractions by using apostrophes correctly.

I will go to the party. *I'll* go to the party.
I am excited about it. *I'm* excited about it.

Try It! Underline the contraction in each sentence. Then write the words from which the contraction is formed.

1. I'll see all my friends at the party for Stella. I will
2. She'll certainly be surprised by the party. she will
3. We've kept the secret very well. we have
4. I know she's going to scream when she sees us. she is
5. Can you imagine how we'll feel when the day finally comes? we will
6. I'm sure we will not know what to do with ourselves in the morning. I am
7. They've been blowing up balloons for hours. they have
8. Are we sure he's not going to tell her? he is
9. Who'll be the first to yell "surprise"? who will
10. I bet it'll be Jay. it will

Write It! Write a dialog between two friends who are planning a surprise party for another friend. Be sure to use contractions correctly.

WHOSE, WHO, WHOM

- An **interrogative pronoun** is a pronoun that introduces an interrogative sentence. *Whose*, *who*, and *whom* are interrogative pronouns.
- Use *who* as the subject of a sentence. Use *whom* as the object of a verb or the object of a preposition.

When you write, be sure to use interrogative pronouns correctly. Do not confuse the pronoun *whose* with the contraction *who's* (*who is*).

Who owns the new car?   To *whom* does the car belong?   *Whose* car is this?

Try It!   Underline the correct pronoun in parentheses.

1. (Who, Whom) invented the first car?
2. To (who, whom) can we give credit?
3. (Whose, Who's) idea was the assembly line?
4. For (who, whom) was the first car created?
5. (Who, Whom) best represents the inventor?
6. From (who, whom) did the plans come?
7. With (who, whom) did Ford work on his plans?
8. (Whose, Who's) financing made the first factory possible?
9. (Who, Whom) did Ford name as his successor?
10. (Whose, Who's) goals were met with the first inexpensive car?

Write It!   Imagine that you will interview a person whose achievements have changed the world. Write a series of questions that you would ask in the interview. Ask a classmate to check your work for correct use of *who*, *whom*, and *whose*.

INTERROGATIVE AND DEMONSTRATIVE PRONOUNS

- An **interrogative pronoun** is a pronoun that introduces an interrogative sentence.
- A **demonstrative pronoun** points out something and stands alone in a sentence.

When you write, do not confuse *who's* (a contraction for *who is*) with the interrogative pronoun *whose*.

Interrogative Pronouns		Demonstrative Pronouns	
who	whose	this	that
whom	which	these	those
what			

Try It!   Underline the correct word in parentheses. Tell whether it is an interrogative pronoun, a contraction, or a demonstrative pronoun.

1. (Who, Whom) are the experts on American pop music?   _interrogative_
2. (Whose, Who's) CD player is that?   _interrogative_
3. (Whose, Who's) going to the concert with me?   _contraction_
4. (That, What) is a very nice oboe.   _demonstrative_
5. (This, These) are excellent seats.   _demonstrative_
6. For (whom, who) are you saving those seats?   _interrogative_
7. (Which, That) singer is the best I've ever heard.   _demonstrative_
8. (What, That) is that loud noise coming from backstage?   _interrogative_
9. (That, Who) is my good friend the guitar player.   _demonstrative_
10. With (whom, who) are you attending the next concert?   _interrogative_

Write It!   Imagine that you are persuading someone to attend a concert with you. What reasons would you use? Write a persuasive paragraph. Use interrogative and demonstrative pronouns in your work.

REFLEXIVE AND INTENSIVE PRONOUNS

- A **reflexive pronoun** directs the action of the verb to the subject.
- An **intensive pronoun** adds emphasis to a noun or pronoun already named.

When you write, you can use reflexive pronouns to intensify a statement. Then the pronoun is an intensive pronoun.

Reflexive Pronouns

Singular	Plural
myself	ourselves
yourself	yourselves
himself, herself, itself	themselves

She reminded *herself* of the curfew. **reflexive**
She *herself* was not interested in the magazine. **intensive**

Try It! Draw one line under each reflexive or intensive pronoun. Then label each as *reflexive* or *intensive*.

1. I myself am not going to the party. _intensive_
2. You can go by yourselves if you wish. _reflexive_
3. Tell him to let himself into the basement. _reflexive_
4. Since they do not want to go, we will be by ourselves. _reflexive_
5. They themselves are not happy about the situation. _intensive_
6. Will they tell her themselves? _reflexive_
7. He himself is the host for the party. _intensive_
8. The basement itself is huge enough for a party. _intensive_
9. Will she allow herself one dance with anyone? _reflexive_
10. I feel sorry for him sitting in the corner by himself. _reflexive_

Write It! Write a description of someone you know. Use reflexive and intensive pronouns in your work.

ADJECTIVES

- An **adjective** modifies or describes a noun or a pronoun.
- A **predicate adjective** follows a linking verb and describes the subject.
- A **participle** is a verb form that can be used as an adjective.

When you write, use colorful adjectives so that your writing will be descriptive.
This is *steamy* weather for May. **adjective**
The weather was *humid*. **predicate adjective**
The *exciting* weather report kept us awake. **participle**

Try It! Underline the adjectives, including participles. Identify the noun or pronoun the adjectives modify.

1. Sunny Florida was hot and sticky. _Florida_
2. Interested tourists strolled through the parks. _tourists_
3. Lazy turtles sunned themselves in metal cages. _turtles, cages_
4. The young children went on a guided tour. _children, tour_
5. The huge, sleek whales leaped in the air. _whales_
6. The whales were black and white. _whales_
7. Did you see that fabulous show? _show_
8. The car was in the last row of the lot. _row_
9. We were tired and weary at the end of the day. _We_
10. The air-conditioned car felt good. _car_

Write It! Describe a trip that you have taken. What did you see? Where did you go? Share your description with a friend. Have your friend identify the adjectives in your description.

105

COMPARATIVE ADJECTIVES

- The **comparative form** of an adjective compares two nouns. Add *er* to many adjectives to form the comparative.
- Use the word *more* to form the comparative of some two-syllable and all three-syllable adjectives.

Do not use *more* with an adjective that ends in *er*.

Adjective	Comparative
tall	taller
active	more active
fascinating	more fascinating

Try It! Underline the correct comparative form in parentheses.

1. In my opinion, London is (interestinger, more interesting) than Paris.

2. Is Big Ben (taller, more tall) than the Eiffel Tower?

3. The Tate Gallery is (more smaller, smaller) than the Louvre.

4. Nonetheless, shopping is (more fun, funner) in Paris.

5. The art is (most accessible, more accessible) in the Tate.

6. But the Tate is (gloomier, more gloomy) than the Louvre.

7. Still, the Louvre is (grander, more grand) in many ways.

8. London's West End is (popularer, more popular) than the Paris Opera.

9. The sculpture in Paris is (more stirring, most stirring) than the sculpture in London.

10. I think the Paris subway is (nicer, more nice) than the London subway.

Write It! Write a descriptive paragraph comparing two places that you like. Then, exchange papers with a classmate and have your classmate make sure that you have used comparative adjectives correctly.

ARTICLES AND PROPER ADJECTIVES

- **Articles** are special kinds of adjectives. *The* is a **definite article**. *A* and *an* are **indefinite articles.**
- A **proper adjective** is formed from a proper noun and begins with a capital letter.

Be sure to capitalize proper adjectives. Remember to use *an* before a noun that begins with a vowel and *a* before a noun that begins with a consonant.

an excellent *Italian* movie   *the German* musician   *a Spanish* aristocrat

Try It! Draw one line under each proper adjective and rewrite it, capitalized. Draw two lines under each definite or indefinite article.

1. At the Food Fair we had many kinds of food and entertainment.

2. Mrs. Russo brought her italian sausages.   Italian

3. My mom supplied mexican tacos and all the trimmings.   Mexican

4. A sixth-grade class made greek salads.   Greek

5. The hungarian polkas had everyone on the dance floor. Hungarian

6. An excited polish woman danced and danced.   Polish

7. Someone donated an entire box of florida oranges.   Florida

8. The Kellys brought irish stew and soda bread.   Irish

9. The only thing missing was chinese food.   Chinese

10. Next year we intend to have an english tea party.   English

Write It! Think of all the foods that originated in other countries. Write a short report about foods that come from around the world. Identify all the articles and proper adjectives in your report.

SUPERLATIVE ADJECTIVES

- The **superlative** form of an adjective compares more than two nouns. Add *est* to many adjectives to form the superlative.
- Add the word *most* to form the superlative of some two-syllable adjectives and all three-syllable adjectives.

Adjective	Superlative
tall	tallest
active	most active
fascinating	most fascinating

Do not use *most* with an adjective that ends in *est*.

Try It! Underline the correct superlative form in parentheses.

1. That was the (more accomplished, most accomplished) pianist I have ever heard.

2. The guests were (most impressed, more impressed) with him of all the performers.

3. The reviewers were (most kindest, kindest) to the soprano.

4. She had the (best, bestest) voice I ever heard.

5. The tenor had the (most sweetest, sweetest) quality.

6. I thought this recital was the (more varied, most varied) of all I have attended.

7. In your view, who had the (more interesting, most interesting) solo?

8. I thought the flute player was the (engagingest, most engaging).

9. She had the (prettiest, most pretty) gown.

10. She played for the (longest, most longest) time.

Write It! What is your favorite kind of music? Write a paragraph that explains why. Make sure that you have used superlative adjectives correctly in your paragraph.

DEMONSTRATIVE ADJECTIVES

- A **demonstrative adjective** points out something and describes a noun by answering the question *which one?* or *which ones?*
- A **demonstrative pronoun** points out a specific person, place, or thing and stands alone in a sentence.

When you write, be sure to use *this* and *these* to point out nearby people, places, and things and to use *that* and *those* to point out people, places, and things that are farther away.

Demonstrative Adjectives: *This* book is fiction. *Those* books are old.

Demonstrative Pronouns: *This* is mine. *Those* are not for sale.

Try It! Draw one line under each demonstrative adjective and two lines under each demonstrative pronoun.

1. This library is over 100 years old.

2. That collection was given to the library last year.

3. Many of those books are first editions.

4. Have you ever seen one of those.

5. These are just beautiful leather bindings.

6. That first edition was signed by the author.

7. Is this book really 75 years old?

8. These books are antique children's books.

9. Look at these colorful illustrations!

10. That part of the library is being painted.

Write It! Work with a partner to write a travel brochure describing a landmark in your city or town. Check your work to make sure you have used demonstrative adjectives and pronouns correctly.

107

COMPARATIVE ADVERBS

- The **comparative form** of an adverb compares two actions. Add *er* or use the word *more* with the adverb.
- Do not use *more* with *er*.

When you write, be sure to use the comparative form correctly. Use *more* with most two-syllable and three-syllable words.

Adverb	Comparative
far	farther
strongly	more strongly

Try It! Underline the correct form of the comparative adverb in parentheses.

1. The hurricane winds blew (more strongly, most stronger) today than yesterday.

2. The sky turned dark (earlier, more earlier) in the day.

3. The rain fell (harder, more hard) than it did yesterday.

4. The waves in the ocean crashed (more wildly, wildlier) than they had earlier.

5. Did the rain fall (more heavily, most heavily) today or yesterday?

6. I think the wind gusted (more severely, most severely) yesterday than it did today.

7. This hurricane traveled (farther, more farther) up the coast

8. The traffic was moving (slowlyer, more slowly) than it was earlier.

9. Electricity was affected (more seriously, most seriously) this time.

10. Are these storms occurring (most frequently, more frequently) than they did before?

Write It! Compare storms that occur in different parts of the country. Write two paragraphs. Then, check your paragraphs for correct use of comparative adverbs.

ADVERBS

- An **adverb** is a word that modifies a verb, an adjective, or another adverb.
- Adverbs answer the questions *how? when? where?* and *to what extent?*

| The horse ran *quickly*. | **how** | The spectators cheered *first*. | **when** |
| The race is held *here*. | **where** | That was *very* fast. | **to what extent** |

When you write, use adverbs to add clarity and detail to your writing.

Try It! Draw one line under each adverb. Draw two lines under the word it modifies.

1. The favorite in the race was very young.

2. She had run yesterday and was extremely fast.

3. Everyone eagerly watched the horses parade around the ring.

4. The young horse appeared last in the parade.

5. Today she would win her biggest competition.

6. Would she run surely and quickly?

7. The crowd was quite impressed with the rider.

8. He smiled happily at the crowds.

9. The horses' coats shone brightly in the sunlight.

10. The race would end triumphantly for the young horse.

Write It! Imagine that you are a reporter at a sports event. In a paragraph, describe the event for a radio broadcast. Exchange paragraphs with a classmate. Identify the adverbs.

SUPERLATIVE ADVERBS

- The **superlative form** of an adverb compares more than two actions. Add *est* or use the word *most* with the adverb.
- Do not use *est* with *most*.

Adverb	Superlative
far	farthest
strongly	most strongly

Be sure to use the superlative form of an adverb correctly in your writing.

Try It! Draw one line under the superlative form of an adverb.

1. Our drama club performed the scene most forcefully of all the groups.

2. The actor performing most daringly of all was a sixth grader.

3. He dressed the most elegantly also.

4. Do they perform comedies most frequently?

5. The sixth-grade performers acted most confidently of all.

6. In the musicals, the seventh graders sang the most beautifully.

7. One drama required the fastest costume change ever.

8. The play was so long, they had the most intermissions ever.

9. The parents were the most excited people in the audience.

10. The ushers behaved the most nervously of all.

Write It! Write a paragraph about your favorite movie or play. Share your paragraph with a friend. Ask your friend to identify superlative adverbs in your work.

ADJECTIVES AND ADVERBS

- Use **adjectives**, including *bad*, *good*, and *real*, to describe nouns and pronouns.
- Use **adverbs**, including *badly*, *well*, and *really*, to modify verbs, adjectives, and other adverbs.
- You can also use *well* as an adjective when referring to someone's health.

The *happy* camper lighted the fire.   **adjective**
The camper sang *happily* by the fire.   **adverb**
The camper saw a *real* cowhand.   **adjective**
He was *really* impressed.   **adverb**

When you write, be sure to use adjectives and adverbs correctly.

Try It! Draw one line under each adjective. Draw two lines under each adverb.

1. The camper plodded slowly up the crooked path.

2. The black horse limped badly.

3. It had a bad sprain in its left front leg.

4. The unhappy camper did not think the horse looked well.

5. Everyone had told the camper to avoid the dangerous pass.

6. He had proudly ignored everyone's advice.

7. Now he was in a real mess.

8. He had really goofed by not paying attention.

9. Would anyone find the lonely camper and the injured horse?

10. Suddenly, he heard good news on his short-wave radio.

Write It! Write a description of a difficulty you once found yourself in. Share your description with a friend. Ask your friend to identify the adjectives and adverbs in your work.

DOUBLE NEGATIVES

- A **double negative** is the incorrect use of two negative words to convey a negative meaning.
- Avoid double negatives by using only one negative word to convey a negative meaning.

In your writing, if you use *not* in a sentence, be sure that you do not use another negative word in that sentence. Remember that some contractions have the word *not* in them.

Incorrect: The highwire artist *did not use no net.*
Correct: The highwire artist *did not use a net.*
Correct: The highwire artist *used no net.*

Try It! Chose the correct word in parentheses.

1. The circus (has, hasn't) hardly been in town a week.

2. The admission fee (is, isn't) nothing to worry about.

3. Nobody (never, ever) has to stand in line for long.

4. You won't see such talented acts (anywhere, nowhere).

5. There (was, wasn't) hardly room for another person in the audience.

6. No one had (never, ever) seen such acts!

7. The spotlight didn't shine on (anyone, no one) but the lion tamer.

8. During his act there (was, wasn't) hardly a sound in the tent.

9. There wasn't (any, no) talking or whispering.

10. Hardly (no one, anyone) left during the intermission.

Write It! What if you participated in an event in which everything went wrong? Write a paragraph about the experience. Check to make sure that you have used no double negatives.

MISPLACED MODIFIERS

- A **modifier** can be a single adjective or adverb, or it can be a phrase, such as a prepositional phrase.
- A modifier should be as close as possible to the word it modifies. A **misplaced modifier** can result in a confusing or misleading sentence.

When you write, be sure that your modifiers add meaning to the words they describe.

Correct: The boy was running *wildly* and almost lost his shoe.
Incorrect: Running *wildly,* the shoes were almost lost.
Correct: The girl *in the blue jacket* saw the robbery.
Incorrect: The girl saw the robbery *in the blue jacket.*

Try It! Underline the misplaced modifiers in the sentences. If the modifier is not misplaced, write **C** next to the sentence.

1. The woman at the checkout stand was alert. _____ C

2. Alert as ever, the robber was sighted by the guard. _____

3. The robber confronted the guard with a mask over his face. _____ C

4. The woman with her hand on the counter paused. _____

5. She brought her hand to the alarm that connected to the police station slowly. _____ C

6. With her hand on the alarm, she had second thoughts. _____

7. Was the man in the funny clothes really a robber? _____ C

8. _____

9. The guard stood looking at the robber shouting "Halt!" _____ C

10. Decisively, she finally pushed the alarm. _____

Write It! Have you ever had to make a quick decision? Write a paragraph telling about that time. How did you reach your decision? Check your work to see that you do not have any misplaced modifiers.

Prepositions

- A **preposition** relates a noun or pronoun to another word in a sentence.
- A **prepositional phrase** is a group of words that begins with a preposition and ends with a noun or a pronoun. That noun or pronoun is called the **object of the preposition**.

When you write, you can use prepositional phrases to describe locations.

The boy looked *under the bed.*   Check *inside the trunk.*

The book bag was *on the table.*   The car is *behind the house.*

Try It! Draw one line under the prepositional phrase. Draw two lines under the object of the preposition.

1. Jason has misplaced his book bag somewhere in the house.

2. He misplaced it sometime after dinner.

3. Is it wedged behind the big bookcase in the hall?

4. I saw him put it on the bookcase.

5. Perhaps he left it outside the house.

6. No, I'm sure it is inside this house.

7. In the meantime, put the books into this briefcase.

8. I will lose my papers among all these books.

9. That report by my sister is very good.

10. I have been upset about this since last night.

Write It! Think of something that you once misplaced. How did you go about finding it? Write a paragraph that tells about this event. Identify the prepositional phrases in your work.

Using Pronouns in Prepositional Phrases

- When the object of a preposition is a pronoun, use an object pronoun.
- Use *me* or *us* last in a compound object of a preposition.
- Do not use a reflexive pronoun when an object pronoun is needed.

When you write, be sure to use object pronouns as objects of prepositions.

Correct: Have you sent the letter to *me?*

Correct: Except for *Bill and me,* no one received the mailing.

Incorrect: Except for me and Bill, no one received the mailing.

Correct: This will not come between *Bill and me.*

Incorrect: This will not come between Bill and myself.

Try It! Underline the correct word or words in parentheses.

1. The glee club sent out a mailing to (us, ourselves).

2. They sent one to (me and Tom, Tom and me).

3. For (Sara and her, her and Sara) they made an exception.

4. Give that sheet music to (he and Tom, Tom and him).

5. Except for (she, her), no one is interested in joining.

6. Between (us, we), I think the club will not survive.

7. We can't keep it going between (us, ourselves).

8. She talked with (my sister and me, me and my sister) about the club.

9. They received donations from (him and I, him and me).

10. She will save the music for (us, ourselves).

11. I hope they give the music stands to (us, we).

Write It! What if you had to raise money for a school club? How would you go about it? Write a paragraph explaining what you would do. Share your paragraph with a classmate. Have your classmate check that you have used the correct pronouns in prepositional phrases.

111

CONJUNCTIONS

- A **coordinating conjunction** connects parts of a sentence or two sentences.
- **Correlative conjunctions** are pairs of words such as *neither/nor* used to connect parts of a sentence or two sentences.
- A **subordinating conjunction** is used to introduce a subordinate clause.

When you write, you add variety to your work by using compound and complex sentences. Be sure to use conjunctions correctly in these sentences.

Bob *and* Joe studied the Vikings.　**coordinating**

The Vikings were fine sailors, *and* they were the first to arrive here.　**coordinating**

Neither Joe *nor* Bob had known much about the Vikings.　**correlative**

After they studied the Vikings, they knew more.　**subordinating**

Try It!　Draw one line under the coordinating conjunctions. Draw two lines under the correlative conjunctions. Write any subordinating conjunctions after the sentence.

1. If the Vikings really landed first, it is quite some story. _____ If

2. There is little physical evidence, and historians disagree about it.

3. Either Bob or Joe will make a report on their findings.

4. The Vikings arrived before Columbus did. _____ before

5. They must have landed in New England if they found grapes there. _____ if

6. They built shelters and scouted the area.

7. Neither the Vikings nor the Indians made headway with an alliance.

8. They wanted to be friendly, but circumstances prevented it.

9. Whenever the weather permitted, the Vikings explored the land. _____ Whenever

10. Bob believes the evidence, but Joe is still unsure.

Write It!　Write a report about the Vikings. Share your report with a friend. Ask your friend to identify the conjunctions in your report.

PREPOSITIONAL PHRASES AS ADJECTIVES AND ADVERBS

- An **adjective phrase** is a prepositional phrase that modifies a noun or a pronoun.
- An **adverb phrase** is a prepositional phrase that may modify a verb.
- An adverb phrase can tell *when, where,* or *why* an action takes place.

When you write, you can use adjective and adverb phrases to add description to your work.

The trees *by the river* are lovely.　**adjective phrase**

Sally went *to the state park.*　**adverb phrase, where?**

She hiked *until sunset.*　**adverb phrase, when?**

The guide asked *about her route.*　**adverb phrase, why?**

Try It!　Draw one line under each adjective phrase. Draw two lines under each adverb phrase.

1. The hiker in the blue shorts was very good.

2. She walked toward the trail quickly.

3. The trail wound through a deep forest.

4. The forest with the huge trees did not frighten her.

5. She hiked over the rough trail easily.

6. She paused at a clearing.

7. A guide for the park service appeared suddenly.

8. The guide pointed to a large group of trees.

9. She looked into the darkness.

10. Behind the tree stood a deer with a speckled tail.

Write It!　Write a story about an adventure you have had or would like to have. Be sure to use prepositional phrases to describe the setting of your adventure and some of the events. Share your story with a friend. Ask your friend to identify the adjective and adverb phrases.

MAKING VERBS AGREE WITH COMPOUND SUBJECTS

- When two or more subjects are joined by *and* or *both . . . and,* the verb is plural.
- When two or more subjects are joined by *or, nor, either . . . or,* or *neither . . . nor,* the verb agrees with the subject that is closest to it.

Remember that a compound subject can be three words.

Tom, Sara, and Joyce *are* in the debate club.
Both Tom and Sara *have been* members for years.
Tom or last year's winner *is* the one to watch.
Neither Sara nor the other winners *worry* Tom.

Try It! Draw one line under the correct form of the verb in parentheses. Draw two lines under the conjunctions.

1. Either Tom or Sara (call, calls) the debate club meeting to order.

2. Beth and I (love, loves) the debate club.

3. A debate or good argument always (intrigue, intrigues) us.

4. Both Tom and Sara (helps, help) to set the agenda for the meeting.

5. This month neither Tom nor Sara (have, has) the time.

6. Therefore, Beth and I (have, has) to do it.

7. Beth or the other members (choose, chooses) the topics.

8. Both Alison and I (ask, asks) for silence.

9. The schoolroom or the auditorium (is, are) a good location for the debate.

10. The principal and three teachers (is, are) the judges.

Write It! Think of an issue that interests you and would be a good debate topic. Write some pros and cons for the issue. If you include any compound subjects in your writing, make sure that your verbs agree with them.

INTERJECTIONS

- An **interjection** is a word or phrase used to express strong feeling.
- Use an exclamation mark after an interjection that stands alone. Use a comma after an interjection that comes at the beginning of a sentence.

The use of interjections can add expression to a character's dialog. Be sure to punctuate interjections correctly.

Common Interjections: *Wow, Ah, Aha, Hooray, Gee, Gosh, Oh, my, Oops*

Wow! Did you see those fireworks?
Wow, the fireworks were spectacular this year.

Try It! Underline the interjection in each sentence.

1. Aha! I knew the fireworks would surprise you.

2. I knew just what your reaction would be. Wow!

3. Hey, I saw you here last year on the Fourth of July.

4. Oh, no, that was two years ago.

5. Oops, I almost spilled my soft drink.

6. Gee, I don't want to miss the finale.

7. Good heavens, look at that beautiful display!

8. The heavens are completely lighted. Hooray!

9. I have never seen anything like it. Gee!

10. Wow, I hope this celebration never ends.

Write It! Get ready for a Fourth of July celebration by designing a poster. Identify any interjections that you use.

SENTENCES AND CLAUSES

- A **simple sentence** has one complete subject and one complete predicate.
- A **compound sentence** has two or more independent clauses that can stand alone as a sentence.
- A **subordinate clause** is a group of words that has a subject and a predicate, but cannot stand alone as a complete sentence.
- A **complex sentence** contains an independent clause and one or more subordinate clauses.

When you write, be sure to use a comma after a subordinate clause at the beginning of a complex sentence.

Simple: *Early explorers were brave.*

Compound: *They explored unknown lands, and they survived.*

Complex: *After they explored an area, they usually mapped it.*

Try It! Write *simple, compound,* or *complex* next to each sentence to tell which kind of sentence it is.

1. Thomas Jefferson asked Meriwether Lewis to lead an expedition. _____ simple

2. The United States had purchased a large parcel of land from France, and it was completely unexplored. _____ compound

3. Although Lewis wanted to go, he did not wish to go alone. _____ complex

4. He asked his friend William Clark, an army officer, to go with him. _____ simple

5. The expedition began its trip in St. Louis, Missouri. _____ simple

6. When they set out, they knew their mission was to find a safe passage to the West. _____ complex

7. They faced many hardships, but they did not give up. _____ compound

8. The trip took 18 months to complete. _____ simple

9. As the group looked at the Pacific Ocean, they were happy. _____ complex

10. After they returned to Washington, they presented President Jefferson with many maps of the area. _____ complex

Write It! Write a diary entry for one of the members of the expedition. Identify simple, compound, and complex sentences in the entry.

ADJECTIVE CLAUSES

- An **adjective clause** is a subordinate clause that modifies, or describes, a noun or pronoun in the independent clause of a complex sentence.
- An adjective clause usually begins with a **relative pronoun** such as *who, whom, which,* or *that.*

When you write, be sure to use commas to set off an adjective clause that is not essential to the meaning of the sentence.

The people who created the sculpture were at the show.

The patrons, who are avid supporters, applauded the artists.

Try It! Underline the adjective clause in each sentence. If the sentence needs commas, add them.

1. The show that opened recently included outstanding sculpture.

2. The pieces, which were over six feet tall, were impressive.

3. The artists who created the pieces worked in marble.

4. The marble, which was imported from Italy, was flawless.

5. The piece that was my favorite was an angel.

6. The owner of the gallery, whom I met in college, was pleased with the show.

7. The refreshments that were served at the reception were delicious.

8. Many of the people who came to the show purchased pieces.

9. The artists, whose work was so well received, beamed.

10. The angel that I liked is still available.

Write It! What kind of art do you like? Write a description of a painting or a piece of sculpture that appeals to you. Exchange your writing with a classmate. Ask your classmate to identify adjective clauses.

114

ADVERB CLAUSES

- A **adverb clause** modifies the verb in the independent clause of a complex sentence.
- An adverb clause usually begins with a **subordinating conjunction**, such as *because, when, although,* or *if.*

When you write, remember to place a comma after a clause that comes at the beginning of the sentence.

Although I was very tired, I continued to practice.
I shot several baskets before I went to bed.

Try It!   Underline the adverb clause in each sentence. If a sentence needs a comma, add it.

1. Because the tournament is soon, I am practicing every night.

2. If we win this tournament, we will go to the state competition.

3. The team plays well when it has practiced regularly.

4. I have been steadily improving ever since I began to practice more.

5. Although the coach still has doubts, I know I am ready to start.

6. Before I go to school, I practice.

7. I also practice when I come home from school.

8. I even practice before I go to bed.

9. If you see Coach Kelly, tell him I am ready.

10. Perhaps he will come to his senses when he sees me play.

Write It!   Write a letter to the editor that expresses your point of view about an issue that is important to you. Identify the adverb clauses in your letter.

NOUN CLAUSES

- A **noun clause** is a subordinate clause that functions as a noun.
- A noun clause can be a subject, a direct object, a predicate noun, or an object of a preposition.
- Some words that introduce noun clauses are *how, that, why, what, when, where, whose,* and *who.*

Subject:	*How I learned to fly is my essay topic.*
Direct Object:	*I will pursue whatever aspect interests me.*
Object of a Preposition:	*I will focus on what I prefer.*
Predicate Noun:	*The field is where I spend my time.*

When you write, you can use noun clauses in the same ways that nouns are used.

Try It!   Underline the noun clause in each sentence. Tell how it is used.

1. Why I love to fly   is obvious.   subject

2. Whoever learns to fly   observes many things.   subject

3. The view from the plane is what intrigues me.   predicate noun

4. I will fly with whoever wants a ride.   object of a preposition

5. The flight plan gave me an idea about
   which route would be best.   object of a preposition

6. My only worry is how I will get there on time.   predicate noun

7. Now I wonder which route I should take.   direct object

8. The Grand Canyon is what I saw.   predicate noun

9. What I really need   is a better map.   subject

10. Which plane I take   depends on the weather.   subject

Write It!   Write a paragraph about something you would like to learn to do. Identify the noun clauses in your work.

Participles and Participial Phrases

Name: _____   Date: _____

- A **participle** is a verb form that can be used as an adjective to modify nouns or pronouns.
- A **participial phrase** is a group of words that includes a participle used as an adjective and other words that complete the meaning.

Remember that the present participle is formed by adding *ing* to a verb and the past participle is formed by adding *ed*. In your writing, be sure to place a comma after a participial phrase that comes at the beginning of the sentence.

Racing to the bus stop, the woman tripped.   **participial phrase**
Embarrassed by her clumsiness, she frowned.   **participial phrase**
The *frowning* woman looked unhappy.   **participle**

Try It! Draw one line under the participle or participial phrase. Draw two lines under the noun or pronoun that the phrase modifies.

1. The interested bystander asked if he could help.
2. An excited bus driver screeched the bus to a stop.
3. Waving him on, the woman sat on a bench.
4. Shrugging with disgust, the bystander boarded the bus.
5. The woman looked at her beautiful imported shoe.
6. Hoping that it wasn't ruined, the woman removed it.
7. Suddenly, a child dressed in a snowsuit appeared.
8. Staring at the woman, the child extended her hand.
9. Looking quite cute, the little girl made the woman feel better.
10. Standing up, the woman shook the little girl's hand.

Write It! Write a story about an embarrassing incident. Share your story with a classmate. Have your classmate identify any participles or participial phrases in your writing.

Gerunds

Name: _____   Date: _____

- A **gerund** is a verb form that ends in *ing* and is used as a noun.
- A **gerund phrase** is a group of words that includes a gerund and other words that complete its meaning.

When you write, you can add variety to your sentences by using gerunds and gerund phrases as subjects and as direct objects.

Running is one of my favorite activities.   **gerund as subject**
She chose *marathon running* as her event.   **gerund phrase as direct object**

Try It! Underline each gerund or gerund phrase. Tell whether it is a **subject** or a **direct object.**

1. Race walking is great fun.   _____ subject
2. Sprinting is my favorite event.   _____ subject
3. Training for the various events is difficult.   _____ subject
4. The instructor likes cheering for the racers.   _____ direct object
5. Watching from the sidelines is fun too.   _____ subject
6. I dislike watching the race from there.   _____ direct object
7. She enjoys winning more than anything else.   _____ direct object
8. Finishing the race will be my biggest triumph.   _____ subject
9. Participating is all I care about.   _____ subject
10. My parents love rooting loudly for the racers.   _____ direct object

Write It! Write a comparison/contrast paragraph that explains the similarities and differences of two sports. Identify the gerunds and gerund phrases in your work.

INFINITIVES

- An **infinitive** is formed with the word *to* and the base form of the verb.
- An **infinitive phrase** includes an infinitive and other words that complete its meaning.

You can use infinitives and infinitive phrases as subjects or direct objects in your sentences when you write.

To sing is a glorious gift. **infinitive-subject**

We plan *to sing* at the concert. **infinitive-direct object**

We decided *to sing loudly* at the finale. **infinitive phrase-direct object**

I am going *to the concert*. **prepositional phrase**

Try It! Draw one line under infinitives and infinitive phrases. Draw two lines under prepositional phrases.

1. Sarah loves to dance.

2. She will go to great lengths for an opportunity.

3. Many people will go to Hayes Stadium for the concert.

4. To see all those people will be fantastic.

5. Thousands plan to attend.

6. To buy tickets may be a problem.

7. We rushed to the box office early.

8. I want to sit in the first row near the band.

9. Do you plan to watch every act?

10. They decided to arrive an hour early.

Write It! What hobby do you like? Write a paragraph about your favorite hobby. Identify any infinitives or infinitive phrases in your work.

END PUNCTUATION

- End **declarative** and **imperative** sentences with a **period**.
- End **interrogative** sentences with a **question mark**.
- End **exclamatory** sentences with an **exclamation mark**.

When you write, be sure to punctuate your sentences correctly.

Declarative: *World War II began in Europe.*

Imperative: *Read the report about the battle.*

Interrogative: *Did you study the causes of the war?*

Exclamatory: *Good grief, the hardships must have been terrible!*

Try It! Add the correct end punctuation to each of the sentences.

1. Germany committed several acts of aggression _._

2. Was Hitler the leader of Germany then _?_

3. The rest of Europe was worried when Hitler marched into Czechoslovakia _._

4. My heavens, Hitler was quite a tyrant _!_

5. France and Great Britain declared war on Germany _._

6. What did the United States do _?_

7. Read your history book to find out _._

8. The United States gave arms and supplies to Great Britain and France _._

9. Did that help the war effort in Europe _?_

10. Goodness, the war years must have been terrible _!_

Write It! What do you know about World War II? Conduct some research about World War II and write a short report about one aspect of the war. Be sure to use correct end punctuation in your report.

COMMAS

- Use **commas** before the conjunction in a compound sentence.
- Use **commas** between the names of cities and states.
- Use a **comma** to separate the day and the year in a date.
- Use **commas** to separate words in a series.
- Use **commas** after introductory words or phrases.
- Use **commas** to set off words in direct address and appositives.

When you write, be sure to use commas after the state and after the year in sentences.

Sam is a good friend, and I spend a lot of time with him.
He lives in Tupelo, Mississippi, on a farm.
He was born on December 21, 1940, in Jackson.
Sam is smart, polite, and kind to me.
No, Sam, the nicest person in the world, does not have brothers or sisters.
You, my friend, will come to dinner when Sam is here.

Try It! Add commas to the following sentences where they are needed.

1. The friends went to the movies, and they saw a great comedy.
2. The plays were great in New York, New York, on Broadway.
3. We made reservations for March 11, 1997, at the hotel.
4. We went to concerts, saw plays, and toured museums.
5. Sam, will you please stop dancing in the aisles.
6. The usher, a man in a green suit, looked annoyed.
7. We can go to dinner, but we don't have time for a play.
8. Sam will return to Jackson, Mississippi, on a jet.
9. He has only two more days here, and then he will have to go home.
10. He will come to visit again on January 5, 1998.

Write It! Write a description of a day that you spent with a friend. What did you do? Where did you go? Be sure to use commas correctly in your writing.

COLONS

- Use a **colon** after the greeting in a business letter.
- Use a **colon** to separate the hour and the minute when you write the time of day.
- Use a **colon** to introduce a list of items that ends a sentence. Use a phrase such as *the following* or *as follows* before the list.

When you write, be sure to use colons correctly when you include lists in your work.

Dear Madam: 7:00 A.M.
Please bring the following: a toothbrush, toothpaste, and two towels.

Try It! Add ten colons where they are needed to this letter.

July 16, 1996
Dear Sir:

I am writing to complain about the treatment I have received from your company regarding an order. I called on Tuesday, December 6, at 9:00 A.M. The message I left at that time was ignored. I called again at 3:00, and one of your assistants was very rude to me. Consequently, I am writing this letter.

Three weeks ago, I ordered the following: a pup tent, two canteens, and a sleeping bag. The instructions I gave on my order were as follows: ship the order overnight mail, pack it in one carton, and deliver it by 10:00 A.M.

That is not the way I received the order. It came three days later at 5:00 P.M. I was not at home so I had to go to the post office at 8:00 A.M. the next day.

At the post office, I was given the following information: the package had been returned to you, and you had refused delivery. The package was lost somewhere in the system.

These are my instructions to you. Please proceed as follows: return my money, tear up my order, and do not send me another catalog.

Yours truly,
An aggravated customer

Write It! Write a business letter of your own. Be sure to use colons correctly.

ITALICS/UNDERLINING

> - Use **italics** or **underlining** to identify the title of a book, a play, a film, a TV series, a magazine, or a newspaper.

Be sure to use italics or underlining correctly when you write reviews of books and films.

Book: *The Incredible Journey*	Magazine: *Time*
Newspaper: *Main Street Journal*	TV series: *Sesame Street*
Film: *Free Willy*	Play: *A Christmas Carol*

Try It! Add underlining where it is needed to the following sentences.

1. Did you see the movie Little Women?

2. It was reviewed in the Washington Post.

3. I watch 60 Minutes every Sunday night.

4. Sally went to see Beauty and the Beast on Broadway.

5. Do you subscribe to Newsweek?

6. Marc Anderson appeared on Jeopardy last week.

7. I read Sarah, Plain and Tall last year.

8. They filmed Home Alone in my neighborhood.

9. Who was the star of Cats?

10. Entertainment Weekly had a review of that film.

Write It! Write a review of a film, book, or play that you have seen recently. Be sure to use italics or underlining correctly in your review.

QUOTATION MARKS

> - Use **quotation marks** before and after a direct quotation.
> - Use **quotation marks** to identify the title of a short story, an essay, a song, a short poem, a book chapter, or a magazine or newspaper article.

Be sure to use end punctuation correctly when you write quotations.

"Please sit down," said the instructor.   "Who will take the roll?" he asked.

John said, "I hope you win the contest."   "Wow, what a speech!" she said.

"My Personal Quest"   "Hey Jude"   "The Necklace"

Try It! Add quotation marks where they are needed to each of the following sentences.

1. Please enter the contest, encouraged the teacher.

2. My essay is called How I Spent the Best Day of My Life.

3. The writing contest is open to all, said the advisor.

4. What are you going to write about? asked Susan.

5. Jake is going to write about his favorite song, In the Good Old Summertime.

6. Who will read my poem? asked John.

7. Sam read The Gift of the Magi by O. Henry.

8. Did you enjoy it? asked Sylvia.

9. That magazine article is called The Way of the World.

10. Bring your poems to my office, said Sarah, before the end of the day.

Write It! Write a short story about a real life adventure. Be sure to use quotation marks for any dialog that you write.

120

APOSTROPHES

- Use an **apostrophe** and an *s* ('s) to form the possessive of a singular noun or a plural noun that does not end in *s*.
- Use an **apostrophe** alone to form the possessive of a plural noun that ends in *s*.
- Use an **apostrophe** and an *s* ('s) to form the possessive of an indefinite pronoun.
- Use an **apostrophe** in a contraction to show where letters have been omitted.

Dorrie's book   the children's room   the actors' roles
anybody's sweater   would + not = wouldn't

When you write, be sure to use apostrophes correctly in possessive nouns.

Try It! Add apostrophes where they are needed in the following sentences.

1. The Andersons' house is on my block.
2. They dont have a very big yard.
3. The childrens tree house is in the backyard.
4. Robs sand box is also back there.
5. The girls' bikes are often found on the driveway.
6. Everybodys toys are in the toy box in the garage.
7. Mr. Anderson doesnt mind all the children.
8. His six brothers' belongings were all over the house.
9. Is this someones jacket?
10. Dont throw that jacket away.

Write It! Write a paragraph describing something that belongs to you. Share your paragraph with a classmate. Ask your classmate to identify where you have used apostrophes correctly.

ABBREVIATIONS

- In both informal and formal writing you may use **abbreviations** for certain organizations and government agencies.
- In informal **writing** and on envelopes, you may use United States Postal Service abbreviations for the names of the states.
- In scientific writing use abbreviations for units of measure. The abbreviation is the same for the singular and plural units.

American Library Association	ALA
Alabama	AL
pound(s)	lb
kilometer(s)	km

In most cases, when your writing is formal, you will not use abbreviations.

Try It! Write the abbreviations for the following.

1. California _____ CA
2. Association for the Prevention of Cruelty to Animals _____ ASPCA
3. inch _____ in.
4. meter _____ m
5. ounce _____ oz
6. New York _____ NY
7. Indiana _____ IN
8. Federal Bureau of Investigation _____ FBI
9. Internal Revenue Service _____ IRS
10. Ohio _____ OH

Write It! Write a paragraph about a science subject that interests you. Be sure to write the correct abbreviations for any units of measure that you use.

PARENTHESES

- Use parentheses for material that is not part of the main statement but is important to include.

To add variety to your writing, you may wish to include material in parentheses to your sentences.

Sarah (who would later win the award) bowed at curtain call.

Try It! Read each sentence. If there is material that should be enclosed in parentheses, add the parentheses.

1. The play that the eighth-graders presented was a huge hit.

2. The comedy (which was adapted from a short story)was so funny.

3. Did you like the first act better than the other two?

4. John (the student to my right)laughed so hard he almost cried.

5. I saw Mr. Lewis wiping tears from his face.

6. The director (who has directed other plays)looked very pleased.

7. The actors were so good in their roles.

8. Jacob (the lead actor)stole the show.

9. He was so funny when he fell over the coffee table.

10. Sarah looked so glamorous in her evening gown.

Write It! Write an explanation of something you know how to do. Be sure to use parentheses correctly in your work.

SYNONYMS

- A **synonym** is a word that has the same or almost the same meaning as another word.

When you write, you can replace a vague or general word in a sentence with a word that is more precise.

Vague: The story was very good.
Precise: The story was very *compelling.*

Try It! Replace the underlined word in each sentence with a synonym that is more precise.   Answers will vary. Possible answers are given.

1. The audience for the storyteller was big.   *immense*

2. The storyteller looked at the audience.   *peered*

3. Their faces showed their anticipation.   *exhibited*

4. Everyone had heard that the storyteller was good.   *marvelous*

5. She had several interesting stories in her repertoire.   *intriguing*

6. The audience wanted to be entertained.   *longed*

7. I thought she wore a very nice costume.   *glamorous*

8. The man next to me had a bouquet of small rosebuds.   *miniature*

9. He threw it on the stage when she began her story.   *tossed*

10. The storyteller's eyes looked appreciatively at the man.   *gazed*

Write It! Write a description of a person you admire. Be sure to include precise nouns, verbs, and adjectives in your work. Share your description with a classmate. Ask your classmate to identify any words that you might replace with more precise synonyms.

121

ANTONYMS

- An **antonym** is a word that has an opposite meaning from another word.

In your writing, you can contrast your ideas by using antonyms.
The general *lost* the battle but *triumphed* by winning the war.

Try It! Underline the two antonyms in each sentence.

1. He was aggressive at first, but became more cautious as time went on.

2. The enemy's attempt was feeble while his was more energetic.

3. The clumsy soldier was no match for the graceful horseman.

4. There was a brief pause in the shooting before the prolonged battle continued.

5. The small force seemed confident even though the outcome of the battle was still uncertain.

6. Suddenly a loud cheer was heard in the hushed forest.

7. Vigorous reinforcements came to replace the tired soldiers.

8. They would not retire in defeat; instead, victory would be theirs.

9. The enthusiastic replacements marched past the listless troops.

10. One sad soldier looked at the happy marching men and smiled.

Write It! Contrast what subject you like best in school this year with the subject you liked best last year. If you use any antonyms in your writing, be sure they are precise.

HOMOGRAPHS

- **Homographs** are words that are spelled the same but have different meanings and sometimes different pronunciations.

When you read, use the context of the sentence to understand the correct meaning of a homograph.

The *bear* frightened the campers.   (an animal)
She could not *bear* the weather.   (endure)

Try It! One word in each sentence is a homograph. Underline the homograph.

1. Her rosy complexion was quite fair.

2. Did you wind the grandfather clock?

3. The famous actress took a bow at the end of the performance.

4. I will study plane geometry next year.

5. If I gain another pound, I don't know what I will do.

6. Is the patient's condition stable?

7. Please board the cruiser right now.

8. She bought a yard of the striped fabric.

9. Send your cousin a get-well note.

10. The count married his true love yesterday.

Write It! Write ten sentences using the homographs from **Try It!** Use another meaning for each homograph in your sentences.

HOMOPHONES

- **Homophones** are words that sound alike but have different spellings and different meanings.

When you write, be sure to check the spelling of homophones.

There are three sisters.
Their story is a famous one.
They're all in love at the same time.

Try It! Underline the correct word in parentheses. Use a dictionary if you need one.

1. Sally (red, read) all the books on the book list.

2. The (feat, feet) that the hero performed was pretty amazing.

3. Is (your, you're) book report ready yet?

4. I will give you (sum, some) extra credit for the report.

5. Stop by my office in one (hour, our).

6. You can (here, hear) my report tomorrow in class.

7. The (hole, whole) class will applaud your effort.

8. (Who's, Whose) going to present first?

9. Ted (or, ore) Sam will read first.

10. I will need a (piece, peace) of paper for notes.

Write It! Use each of the homophones that you did not underline in **Try It!** in a new sentence. Share your sentences with a classmate. Ask your classmate to check your use of homophones.

CONTEXT CLUES

- The **context** of a sentence can sometimes help you to figure out the meaning of an unfamiliar word. The context includes the other words in the sentence or in nearby sentences.

When you come across an unfamiliar word in your reading, use the other words in the sentence as clues to help you determine the word's meaning.

The *teeming* street scene was filled with busy crowds.

The words *busy* and *crowds* are clues to the meaning of the word *teeming.*

Try It! Write the meaning of each underlined word. Then use a dictionary to check your work.   Suggested meanings are given.

1. She whispered <u>furtively</u> even in the middle of the free-
   flowing and open conversation.   __in an unnoticed way__

2. Her stare was as <u>frigid</u> as ice.   __cold__

3. His trusty backpack accompanies him on every <u>excursion</u>
   that he takes.   __trip__

4. Have you ever taken a <u>transatlantic</u> cruise to England?   __across the Atlantic__

5. The trip actually cost a <u>pittance</u>, compared to the more
   expensive trips.   __very small amount__

6. I was completely <u>disheartened</u> by the sad state of affairs. __discouraged__

7. She tells many <u>anecdotes</u> about all of her travel
   experiences.   __stories__

8. Sometimes she appears <u>gullible</u> because she believes
   anything you tell her.   __easily lied to or taken in__

9. He had many <u>exploits</u> on his island journey.   __adventures__

10. She was completely <u>dauntless</u> in the face of many of
    the dangers she had on her trip.   __fearless__

Write It! Find a newspaper article and circle five words that are unfamiliar to you in it. Try to use context clues to tell the meaning of the unfamiliar words. Check a dictionary to see how accurate you were. Then use each word in a sentence.

123

SPECIFIC NOUNS

- Using **specific nouns** makes your writing more interesting and helps the reader to picture exactly what you want to convey.

When you write, use specific nouns to focus your thoughts and to state your ideas clearly on paper.

Less Specific: My *dog* barked at the *bird*.
More Specific: My *terrier* barked at the *robin*.

Try It!   Change the underlined noun in each sentence to a more specific noun. Answers will vary. Possible answers are given.

1. The flowers in the garden were lovely.   roses

2. I saw a beautiful bird in the birdbath.   cardinal

3. My pet was intrigued by the grassy meadow.   poodle

4. Will you pick a bunch of wildflowers?   bluebonnets

5. You can bring them into the house.   mansion

6. The man will arrange them into a beautiful display.   gardener

7. We can put the flowers in the room.   library

8. The people will see them when they come in the door.   guests

9. I hope everyone will enjoy the party.   gala

10. We will meet in the other room.   study

Write It!   Write a paragraph describing a party you have had or attended. Make sure that you use specific nouns in your work.

TROUBLESOME WORDS

- Some words, such as *good* and *well*, have very specific rules about their usage. Use *good* as an adjective to describe nouns. Use *well* as an adverb to tell about verbs. Use *well* when talking about health.
- Other words, such as *there*, *their*, and *they're*, have very different meanings. Use *there* to mean a place. Use *their* to show possession. Use *they're* as a contraction to stand for *they are*.
- The words *to*, *two*, and *too* are sometimes confused. Use *to* to introduce a prepositional phrase or an infinitive. Use *two* as a number. Use *too* as an adverb meaning *also* or a *degree of something*.

When you write, watch out for words that are often confused. Check your dictionary if you need help.

It was a *good* paper.   He wrote very *well*.   The boy felt *well*.
Put it over *there*.   Is that *their* car?   *They're* coming today.
Give it *to* me.   I have *two* cookies.   I will have one, *too*.

Try It!   Underline the correct word in parentheses.

1. The patient said that she was feeling very (good, well).

2. She had been a (good, well) patient for several weeks.

3. Did he do (good, well) on the test?

4. I want to sit (there, their).

5. (They're, Their) a very good example for us.

6. She did (two, to) assignments while I watched television.

7. I think you are spending (too, to) much time with her.

8. Will you give the report (to, too) her tomorrow?

9. Have they given you (their, there) assignment yet?

10. I hope I get a very (good, well) grade on my test.

Write It!   Write a paragraph about something that you do very well. Share your paragraph with a classmate. Ask your classmate to tell you if you have used any of the troublesome words from the lesson incorrectly.

VIVID VERBS

- **Vivid verbs** express action precisely and clearly.

When you write, use vivid verbs to help your actions come alive and to help your reader to picture exactly what's happening.

Less Vivid: We *ran* out of the house.

More Vivid: We *dashed* out of the house.

Try It!   Change each underlined verb in the sentence to a more vivid verb.

1. We <u>went</u> to the very exciting race. — ran
2. I <u>saw</u> the horses at the starting gate. — spied
3. They <u>left</u> from the gate at the shot of a pistol. — charged
4. The horses <u>ran</u> around the track. — galloped
5. The two lead horses <u>were</u> neck and neck. — raced
6. The crowd <u>yelled</u> madly. — screamed
7. The galloping horses <u>scared</u> me. — terrified
8. My friend <u>looked</u> at me with alarm. — stared
9. When my horse <u>went</u> across the finish line, I could not look. — sprinted
10. I <u>found</u> my winning ticket in the bottom of my purse. — unearthed

Write It!   Write a story about an adventure you have had or would like to have. Be sure to use vivid verbs in your story.

COLORFUL ADJECTIVES

- **Adjectives** can add sensory details to your writing. Sensory details refer to one or more of the five senses—sight, hearing, touch, taste, or smell.

Sensory words can make your writing more effective as readers of your writing will re-create in their minds the experience you describe.

The children looked in the window.

The *eager, young* children looked in the *decorated store* window.

Try It!   Add some colorful adjectives to these sentences.   Possible answers are given.

1. The shops were filled with merchandise. — busy shops; fabulous merchandise
2. The floor with toys was enchanting. — fantastic toys
3. The boys and girls looked at the toys. — eager boys; excited girls
4. On the fifth floor were the games and videos. — exciting videos
5. The shoppers strolled through the store. — happy shoppers; bustling store
6. They bought things for their families. — several things; young families
7. Did you see that sweater? — pink sweater
8. The ties were quite lovely. — plaid
9. That doll would be perfect for my sister. — pretty; baby
10. I can't wait to wrap the presents. — beautiful

Write It!   Write a paragraph that describes the best gift you ever received. Be sure to include colorful adjectives in your description.

125

EXCITING ADVERBS

Name: _____ Date: _____

- **Exciting adverbs** can add details to your writing that tell *how, when,* and *where.*

Use exciting adverbs whenever possible to make your writing come alive for your reader.

I went to the park.

I *reluctantly went* to the *park yesterday.*

Try It! Add some exciting adverbs to these sentences.

Possible answers are given.

1. Many children played in the park.   played happily
2. The children looked for their toys.   looked everywhere
3. Will you see the babysitter?   babysitter today
4. The young girl smiled at the grandmother.   smiled sweetly
5. The little boy looked strong.   very strong
6. He pushed the swing for his sister.   gladly pushed
7. Tell the noisy children to be quiet.   very quiet
8. I will be going home.   home soon
9. She plays with the other children.   plays often
10. I watched her toss the ball.   carefully toss

Write It! Write a paragraph about your idea of what is fun. Be sure to use exciting adverbs in your paragraph.

79

PREFIXES

Name: _____ Date: _____

- **A prefix** is a word part added to the beginning of a base word.
- A prefix changes the meaning of the base word to which it is added.

In your writing, be sure to use the correct prefix to convey your meaning.

Common Prefix	Meaning	Example
de	from, down	depress
inter	between	intercity
pre	before	precede
re	again, back	review
in	without, not	inexpensive
un	not, opposite of	uninformed

Try It! Underline each word that has a prefix. Write the meaning of the word.

1. I think that book was totally <u>uninteresting</u>.   not interesting
2. I will <u>review</u> it tomorrow.   look at again
3. It's a science fiction book about <u>interplanetary</u> warfare.   between planets
4. Did you <u>preview</u> it before you bought it?   look at before
5. I think the purchase of it is <u>indefensible</u>.   can't be defended
6. I will <u>reevaluate</u> the book.   assess again
7. She <u>prepaid</u> the costs of shipping the book.   paid in advance
8. The writing is totally <u>incomprehensible</u>.   not able to be comprehended
9. I'm sorry I bought *Intergalactic Terror.*   between galaxies
10. I will <u>return</u> it immediately.   give back

Write It! Use each of the underlined words from **Try It!** in a sentence of your own. Exchange papers with a classmate. Have your classmate find the words in your sentences and tell you what they mean.

80

SUFFIXES

- **A suffix** is a word part added to the end of a base word. A suffix changes the meaning of the base word to which it is added. It also changes the part of speech of the base word.

When you write, remember that a suffix changes a word's meaning.

Suffix	Meaning	Example
an (noun)	one that is of	American
er, or, ist (noun)	one who is or does	teacher
ion (noun)	act, state, or result of	protection
able (adjective)	able to	readable
ful (adjective)	full of	sorrowful
ly (adjective)	like	queenly
ly (adverb)	like	busily

Try It! Underline each word that has a suffix. Then tell the meaning of the word. Use a dictionary if necessary.

1. I went on a European trip. _____ of Europe

2. I met a researcher from *National Geographic.* _____ one who does research

3. The guide was quite helpful with the tour. _____ full of help

4. He made sure I made my connection. _____ act of connecting

5. The friendly bus driver gave me a lift. _____ like a friend; one who drives

6. The path to the top of the cliff was manageable. _____ able to be managed

7. I met another American tourist on the trip. _____ of America; one who tours

8. She was a guest speaker at one of the lectures. _____ one who speaks

9. Her talk was unbelievable. _____ not able to be believed

10. I felt her deep concentration on her subject. _____ act of concentrating

Write It! Use each of the underlined words from **Try It!** in a sentence. Identify the suffixes in the words in your sentences.

IMAGERY AND PERSONIFICATION

- **Imagery** is the use of words to create pictures, or images, in the reader's mind.
- **Personification** is a comparison in which human traits are given to objects, ideas, or animals.

You can make your writing more vivid and colorful by using imagery and personification.
Imagery: My trip across the *blazing sands* of Egypt was memorable.
Personification: My trusty sword, *Ahmed*, was always by my side.

Try It! Underline and label examples of *imagery* and *personification* in the following sentences.

1. On my trip around the world I saw islands that were no bigger than tiny dots from the air. _____ imagery

2. The green foliage in the rain forest was dripping with dew. _____ imagery

3. My red jeep, nicknamed Tillie, never failed me. _____ personification

4. She made it over mountains and through muddy streams. _____ personification

5. The muddy streams surged sluggishly through the ravines. _____ imagery

6. Tillie got a little water-logged, but she kept on going. _____ personification

7. The green canopy over my head shut out most of the light. _____ imagery

8. In the rain forest a green calm and quiet prevailed. _____ imagery

9. I left Tillie waiting alone in a clearing and proceeded on foot. _____ personification

10. Tillie was upset, but I had to enter this place on my own. _____ personification

Write It! Write a description of a special place that you know. In your description try to use *imagery* and *personification* to make your writing vivid and colorful.

ALLITERATION AND REPETITION

- **Alliteration** is the repetition of the same initial sound, usually of a consonant, in a series of words.
- **Repetition** involves repeating words, phrases, or even whole lines.

When you write, you can use *alliteration* and *repetition* to make your writing musical and catchy and to stand out in the reader's mind.

Alliteration: The *nice, neat knick-knack* shelf is for sale.

Repetition: *"Buy it! Buy it!"* said the radio announcer.

Try It! Underline and label the examples of alliteration and repetition in the following sentences.

1. There are fabulous finds in the antique store. _____ alliteration
2. Radiant red radios are on a shelf in the back. _____ alliteration
3. In the front on the display case are pretty pink pitchers . _____ alliteration
4. A parrot in a cage says, "Howdy, howdy, to you." _____ repetition
5. Miniature motor cars are in a basket up front. _____ alliteration
6. Beaded ball gowns hang from the walls. _____ alliteration
7. The delightful dolls with satin sashes catch my eye. _____ alliteration
8. They sit at a table on which there are tiny teacups. _____ alliteration
9. Each corner of the shop beckons, "Come here, come here." _____ repetition
10. I cannot leave without that set of brass buttons . _____ alliteration

Write It! Write an ad for a product. Your product can be real or imaginary. Use *alliteration* and *repetition* in your ad to make it catchy.

IDIOMS

- An **idiom** is an expression whose meaning cannot be grasped from the meaning of the individual words comprising it.
- Some idioms are considered perfectly appropriate for formal writing, but some are considered more appropriate for informal speech and writing.

The use of idioms can make the dialog in your writing more authentic and interesting.

The bus driver yelled, *"Step on it!"* to the boy.

Try It! Underline the idioms in the following sentences.

1. I ran across an old friend on the bus today.
2. We had hit it off immediately when we last saw each other.
3. However, now she seemed to be a bit full of herself.
4. We used to hit the books together when we last knew each other.
5. Somewhere along the way she lost her head.
6. She is now nearly always on the go.
7. You really have to shake a leg to keep up with her.
8. She will run you ragged if you don't watch out.
9. I really couldn't get a handle on what she was saying.
10. I was totally at sea by the time we parted.

Write It! Make a list of idioms that you know or use some from **Try It!** Write a conversation between two people who speak in idioms. Share your work with a friend and have your friend define the idioms.

SIMILE AND METAPHOR

- A **simile** uses the word *like* or *as* to compare one thing (person, animal, idea) to another.
- A **metaphor** is a comparison in which one of two things is said to be the other.

Using similes and metaphors in your writing can make it more vivid and colorful.

Simile: *The river is like a shining ribbon.*

Metaphor: *The river is a winding snake.*

Try It! Underline and label the *similes* and *metaphors* in the following sentences.

1. My trip to the West was like a bad dream.   simile

2. The plane ride to Denver was a nightmare.   metaphor

3. The whir of the propeller was like a pounding drill.   simile

4. My head felt as big as a beach ball when we landed.   simile

5. The elevation made my heart beat like a hammer.   simile

6. The mountain trail was as narrow as a thread.   simile

7. The night air was a cold, wet blanket over my head.   metaphor

8. My prepared food tasted like wet cardboard.   simile

9. The horse I rode was as stubborn as a mule.   simile

10. Civilization was a long-awaited gift.   metaphor

Write It! Write a description of something that did not turn out as you had expected. Share your work with a classmate. Ask your classmate to identify any similes or metaphors in your work.

129